THE RUGBY QUIZ BOOK

THE RUGBY QUIZ BOOK

Compiled by Adam Pearson

APEX PUBLISHING LTD

First published in 2008 by
Apex Publishing Ltd
PO Box 7086, Clacton on Sea, Essex, CO15 5WN, England
www.apexpublishing.co.uk

Copyright © 2008 by Adam Pearson
The author has asserted his moral rights

British Library Cataloguing-in-Publication Data
A catalogue record for this book
is available from the British Library

ISBN HARDBACK: 1-906358-17-6   978-1-906358-17-4

Typeset in 10.5pt Chianti Bdlt Win95BT

Cover Design: Siobhan Smith

Printed and bound in Great Britain by
the MPG Books Group

For:
Ian Coughtrey
And
Penarth Rugby Football Club

Also:
Nigel Harris
And
Isle of Wight Rugby Football Club

INTRODUCTION

I was introduced to rugby in the mid-seventies when I used to watch my stepfather play for the Isle of Wight team at Wootton Recreation Ground. I remember a lot of mud, blood and the ever-present essence of Deep Heat. There is a memory that sticks in my mind of the horrific sight of naked burly men striding around the dressing room area after the match. Matches were usually followed by a big session at the bar and a lot of tribal banter. I was a football fan primarily, so I would spend the time listening to the radio and being frustrated at the continual reports that either Keegan or Toshak had just scored for Liverpool.

I didn't get to play rugby until I moved to Penarth in Wales where, at Stanwell Comprehensive School, it was the number one sport. In fact they didn't even have a football team, but we did play at break time with a tennis ball. Rugby is like a religion in Wales and if you aren't any good at the sport you're regarded as a bit of an outcast. I was English as well, so it was doubly hard for me. Once in a match I picked up the ball from the scrum and ran for the line to score a try only to be moaned at by my teammates because I'd had plenty of time to plant the ball under the posts instead of in the corner. The mistake cost us the conversion.

During my time in Penarth I grew to love the game and I became a season ticket holder at Penarth RFC where I witnessed one of its last annual matches against the Barbarians. It was an event that the town was very proud of and it was a dreadful shame when the fixture was scrapped. I also travelled to an away match against Bridgend where I met Welsh Rugby stars J.P.R. Williams and Steve Fenwick.

In a memorable match against England, Welsh hard man

Paul Ringer was sent off for violent conduct. That week he played for Llanelli at Penarth where I was thrilled to meet him in the clubhouse.

I used to skive off school until I realised it would get me into too much trouble and I would travel to Cardiff and sit in the stands at the old national stadium known as Cardiff Arms Park. Once I ran onto the pitch and imagined scoring a try. I saw a match there once between Cardiff RFC and New Zealand All Blacks; it was a great occasion.

In those days Wales had a great reputation and it was usually a miserable time for me when England was beaten by them. That was the case when I left the Principality in 1982 and returned to the Isle of Wight and rather left rugby behind me in favour of football. Then 2003 came and England did quite well in the World Cup. Most of the tournament passed me by. I picked it up at the quarter-final stage, but I was driving on the day of the final and had to watch the match on a small television in the car while parked in a lay-by. It was nonetheless one of the most memorable and proudest moments of my life.

Although my memories of following rugby are of the Union variety, I have always been aware of Rugby League and its fanatical following in the North of England. I could not compile a book on rugby without including both codes. I hope there is plenty within the following pages to entertain all fans of this fantastic sport.

Best wishes
Adam Pearson

ORIGINS

1. In what year was the first set of football rules written?

2. In what year was the Rugby Football Union formed?

3. In what year was Rugby League formed as the Northern Rugby Football Union?

4. What is the name of the world's oldest Rugby Club that was not part of a school or university?

5. Who was the man who published a letter in the papers to arrange a meeting of clubs that wished to play the rugby-type football game and subsequently resulted in the creation of Rugby Union?

6. In what year was the first international rugby match played?

7. How many players were there in a Rugby Union team until the number was reduced to fifteen in 1877?

8. In what year was the antiquated Goal From Mark rule dropped from the rules of Rugby Union?

9. In what year did the Northern Rugby Football Union become known as Rugby Football League?

10. In what year was the oval shape of rugby balls made compulsory?

WILLIAM WEBB-ELLIS

11. In what year was William Webb-Ellis born?

12. In what year was William Webb-Ellis alleged to have run with a football, legendarily making himself the creator of Rugby Football?

13. When William Webb-Ellis left Rugby School, which college did he join?

14. After graduation, what career did William Webb-Ellis adopt?

15. Which co-founder of the *Guinness Book of Records* rediscovered William Webb-Ellis's grave in Menton in Alpes Maritimes, France, in 1958?

16. What is the name of the man who is responsible for the story of William Webb-Ellis running with the ball when he included the tale in a letter to *The Meteor* (The Rugby School magazine) in 1876?

17. In 1895 The Old Rugbeian Society investigated the claim that William Webb-Ellis initiated the game. Who was the author of *Tom Brown's Schooldays* who was asked to comment on his time at Rugby School in the 1830s?

18. In what county was William Webb-Ellis born?

19. In what year did William Webb-Ellis pass away?

20. At what battle was William Webb-Ellis's father, James, killed in 1811?

RUGBY UNION WORLD CUP 1987

21. Who hosted the 1987 World Cup?

22. How many nations took part in the 1987 World Cup?

23. Which nation did New Zealand beat 70-6 in the opening game of the 1987 World Cup?

24. Who won the Pool 1 match between the USA and Japan?

25. Which New Zealand player was the top individual points scorer in the 1987 World Cup?

26. Who scored three tries for England against Japan in their Pool 1 match in the 1987 World Cup?

27. Who scored Wales's first try of the 1987 World Cup against Ireland in Pool 2?

28. New Zealand and which other nation qualified for the 1987 World Cup quarter-finals from Pool 3?

29. In Pool 4 Scotland drew 20-20 with which nation in the 1987 World Cup?

30. Who made 16 conversions in two matches for Scotland against Romania and Zimbabwe in Pool 4 in the 1987 World Cup?

BRITISH AND IRISH LIONS

31. In what year did The Lions play their first match against Otago?

32. Who is the player that scored 274 points during his time with The Lions?

33. Who captained The Lions when they beat Australia in 1989?

34. Who captained The Lions when they beat New Zealand in 1971?

35. Which player has made the most appearances (71) for The Lions?

36. Who captained The Lions during the 2005 tour of New Zealand?

37. In what year did the last amateur Lions tour take place?

38. In what year did The Lions last win a series?

39. Who coached The Lions on three consecutive tours (1989, 1993 and 1997)?

40. Who scored the most points for The Lions during the 2005 tour of New Zealand?

HISTORY OF RUGBY LEAGUE

41. What is the name of the Huddersfield hotel where the meeting that resulted in the formation of the Northern Rugby Football Union was held?

42. What word was used to describe the dispute between professional and amateur rugby?

43. In what year was the first ever Challenge Cup Final played?

44. Which positions are missing from a 13 man Rugby League side but are present in a 15 man Union team?

45. Which club won the first Challenge Cup final?

46. In what year was the first Challenge Cup final played at Wembley?

47. Which club won the first Rugby League championship in 1896?

48. Who was the controller of BBC2 who decided to televise The Rugby League Floodlit Trophy in the 1960s?

49. In what year was the number of tackles in an attack most recently set to 6?

50. In what year was the Sin Bin rule introduced in Australia?

GARETH EDWARDS

51. In which Welsh town was Gareth Edwards born?

52. In what year did Gareth Edwards first play for Wales?

53. In what year did Gareth Edwards score 'That Try' for the Barbarians against The All Blacks at Cardiff Arms Park?

54. In what position did Gareth Edwards play?

55. For which club did Gareth Edwards play?

56. Which commentator said the following memorable words as Gareth Edwards scored 'That Try' for The Barbarians gainst The All Blacks: "Kirkpatrick to Williams. This is great stuff. Phil Bennett covering, chased by Alistair Scowan. Brilliant! Oh, that's brilliant! John Williams, Brian Williams, Pullin, John Dawes. Great dummy! David, Tom David, the half-way line. Brilliant by Quinnell. This is Gareth   Edwards. A dramatic start. What a score!"

57. How old was Gareth Edwards when he became Wales's youngest ever captain?

58. Where is there a statue of Gareth Edwards?

59. What is Gareth Edwards' middle name?

60. When Gareth Edwards took over as team captain of the BBC's *A Question of Sport* in 1979, who was his opposing captain?

ENGLAND

61. In what year did England first play The All Blacks?

62. In what year was the song 'Swing Low Sweet Chariot' first sung at an England match?

63. Against which of the Six Nations does England have the highest win percentage (57.5%)?

64. Which player has scored the most points for England as of 2007?

65. Against which nation did England achieve its biggest winning margin of 134-0 in 2001?

66. In 1998 England lost 76-0 against which nation?

67. Which player held the record for winning the most caps for England in 2007 (118 caps)?

68. Which player scored 49 tries for England during his career?

69. Who captained England during the 2007 World Cup?

70. Who did Sir Clive Woodward replace as England coach?

THE CHALLENGE CUP

71.   After Wembley Stadium was closed, which venue
       staged the next Challenge Cup final?

72.   In 1953-54 the Challenge Cup final between
       Warrington and Halifax went to a replay that holds the
       record for the highest attendance in a Challenge Cup
       final. What city's stadium crammed in 102,569
       people?

73.   What is the name of the trophy that is presented to the
       man of the match in the Challenge Cup final?

74.   Which team did Castleford Tigers beat 15-14 in the
       1986 Challenge Cup final?

75.   Which football stadium staged the 1981-82 Challenge
       Cup final replay between Hull and Widnes?

76.   Can you name the five nations that enter teams into
       the Challenge Cup competition?

77.   Who, in 2006, became the first player in Rugby League
       history to collect a third Man of the Match award in a
       Challenge Cup final?

78.   How many Challenge Cup finals have been contested
       over three matches and decided on aggregate?

79.   Which club won the 1966-67 Challenge Cup final?

80.   Wigan holds the record for the most consecutive
       Challenge Cup wins. How many?

THE BARBARIANS

81.   Which Welsh club did the Barbarians used play every Good Friday until 1986?

82.   Which player had made the most appearances for the Barbarians as of 2007?

83.   In what year did the Barbarians play their first match?

84.   The Barbarians had their biggest win and biggest defeat against the same team. Which one?

85.   Which man inspired the formation of the Barbarians?

86.   Gareth Edwards scored what is known as 'That Try' for the Barbarians against The All Blacks, but what was the final score of that match?

87.   Against which club do the Barbarians traditionally play a Boxing Day fixture?

88.   Which hotel was the nearest thing the Barbarians had to a home because that is where the team stayed during their Easter tour of Wales?

89.   What is the team motto of the Barbarians, given by W.J. Carey (former Bishop of Bloemfontein)?

90.   Which seven nations are featured on the 1927 Barbarian crest?

TWICKENHAM

91. In which London borough is Twickenham Stadium situated?

92. Twickenham Stadium is affectionately known as Twickers and which other nickname?

93. In what year was Twickenham Stadium opened?

94. What was the capacity of Twickenham Stadium in 2007?

95. In what year did the RFU make Twickenham its home?

96. In wat year did Twickenham first host a Rugby League match?

97. Who won the first Rugby League Challenge Cup final to be played at Twickenham Stadium?

98. Which club won the last Rugby League Challenge Cup Final to be played at Twickenham in 2006?

99. In what year was the Museum of Rugby established?

100. What was the name of the infamous Twickenham streaker of 1982?

HULL KINGSTON ROVERS

101.   What is the name of Hull KR's home ground?

102.   In what year did Hull KR open its current home?

103.   In what season did Hull KR first win the Rugby League Championship?

104.   In what season did Hull KR win the BBC2 Floodlit Trophy?

105.   In what season did Hull KR win its one and only Challenge Cup?

106.   In what season did Hull KR last win the Rugby League Premiership?

107.   From what Rugby Union club did Hull KR sign Chev Walker?

108.   Which Australian Hull KR player retired in 2007?

109.   What appears three times on the Hull KR crest?

110.   What is the nickname of Hull KR?

WORLD CUP 1991 (UNION)

111. Which player scored the most points in the 1991 World Cup?

112. Which nation represented Asia in the 1991 World Cup?

113. England finished second in Pool A in the 1991 World Cup, but who topped the group?

114. Which nation did Italy beat 30-9 in Pool A of the 1991 World Cup?

115. France won Pool D of the 1991 World Cup, but who finished second in the group?

116. Who finished second to Australia in Pool C of the 1991 World Cup above Wales, who failed to qualify for the quarter-finals?

117. Who was Wales' top scorer in the 1991 World Cup?

118. Whom did Australia beat 19-18 in the 1991 World Cup quarter-final?

119. Who scored the decisive drop goal for England in the 1991 World Cup semi-final against Scotland?

120. Who scored the only try of the 1991 World Cup final for Australia against England?

JONNY WILKINSON

121. Against which nation did Jonny Wilkinson score his 1000th international point?

122. In which county was Jonny Wilkinson born?

123. In what two rugby positions does Jonny Wilkinson play?

124. For what club did Jonny Wilkinson debut in 1998?

125. Whom did Jonny Wilkinson replace at his club when that player became a coach?

126. For what newspaper does Jonny Wilkinson occasionally write a column?

127. In December 2005 Jonny Wilkinson was awarded an honorary doctorate in Civil Law by which university?

128. In what year did Jonny Wilkinson win the BBC Sports Personality of the Year award?

129. With which foot did Jonny Wilkinson kick the winning drop goal in the 2003 World Cup final?

130. Jonny Wilkinson appeared in advertisements with David Beckham, advertising what brand name?

EDDIE WARING

131. In what year was Eddie Waring born?

132. On what '70s television game show was Eddie Waring a co-presenter alongside Stuart Hall?

133. What was Eddie Waring's catchphrase?

134. What Rugby League club did Eddie Waring once manage?

135. In what television show did Eddie Waring guest as a dancing sailor?

136. Which impersonator was best known for imitating Eddie Waring?

137. What was Eddie Waring's famous quote when in 1968 Wakefield Trinity Rugby League player Don Fox made a feeble kick, missing from in front of the posts during the Challenge Cup final against Leeds, the miss handing the cup to his opponents?

138. What was Eddie Waring's usual statement when a player was sent off?

139. In what year did Eddie Waring retire from sports commentary?

140. In what year did Eddie Waring sadly pass away?

WOMEN'S RUGBY

141. In what year was a female rugby tour to New Zealand cancelled due to public outcry?

142. Maria Eley played fullback at Cardiff Arms Park on 16 December 1917, when Cardiff Ladies beat Newport 6-0 in a wartime charity match. How old was she when she passed away in 2007?

143. In what year was the first Women's Rugby Union league formed in Australia?

144. In what year was the first women's national league and cup competition established in the UK?

145. In what year was the Irish WRFU first officially recognised by the Irish Rugby Football Union?

146. In what year was the first Women's Rugby World Cup held?

147. Running on from the previous question, which nation staged the event?

148. Running on from the previous question, which nation won the event?

149. Which nation finished as runner-up in the first Women's Rubgy World Cup?

150. Which nation has won the Women's Rugby World Cup in 1998, 2002 and 2006?

THE ALL BLACKS

151. What is the colour of New Zealand's change kit shirts?

152. Which New Zealand player won 92 caps between 1986 and 1997?

153. New Zealand's largest win was 145-7 against which nation?

154. New Zealand's worst defeat was 28-7 against which nation?

155. Which New Zealand player has scored the most tries for his nation as of 2007?

156. What is the name of the Maori dance performed by the New Zealand team prior to kick-off?

157. What New Zealand player has scored the most points for his nation as of 2007?

158. In what year did New Zealand first perform a Maori dance during a tour of New South Wales?

159. Who set a record for the most tries in a calendar year for New Zealand in 2003?

160. Who was the New Zealand captain in 2007?

CATALAN DRAGONS

161. What is the full name of the Catalan Dragons' Rugby League club?

162. In what year were the Catalan Dragons founded?

163. What is the name of the Calatan Dragons' home ground?

164. In which country are the Catalan Dragons based?

165. Who was the Catalan Dragons' Australian coach in 2007?

166. Which club did the Catalan Dragons beat in the semi-final to become the first non-English club ever to reach the Challenge Cup final in 2007?

167. In which years did the Catalan Dragons win the Lord Rugby Cup?

168. What two clubs merged to form the Catalan Dragons?

169. What is the name of the Catalan Dragons' Australian fullback?

170. When the Catalan Dragons joined the Super League, how many years was the club exempt from relegation?

CARDIFF ARMS PARK

171. In what year was the British Empire and Commonwealth Games held at Cardiff Arms Park?

172. In 1993 Cardiff Arms Park staged the WBO World Heavyweight title fight between Lennox Lewis and who?

173. True or false: Cardiff Arms Park was actually the name of its neighbour, not the National Stadium that it was always mistaken for?

174. What river did the West Stand of the National Stadium overlook?

175. What is the name given to the only remaining section of the North Stand of the old National Stadium that is now part of the Millennium Stadium?

176. Which sporting attraction previously occupied the land where the National Stadium Cardiff Arms Park was built?

177. Who owned Cardiff Arms Park National Stadium until the WRU took it over in 1968?

178. What was Cardiff Arms Park named after?

179. What was the original name of the park where Cardiff Arms Park was built?

180. What was the capacity of Cardiff Arms Park National Stadium when it closed?

RORY UNDERWOOD

181. What is the name of Rory Underwood's England international brother?

182. What club did Rory Underwood play for between 1983 and 1997?

183. What was Rory Underwood's occupation while he was an England international?

184. In what year was Rory Underwood born?

185. Where was Rory Underwood born?

186. How many England caps did Rory Underwood win?

187. At which club did Rory Underwood end his playing career?

188. In what position did Rory Underwood play?

189. Rory Underwood scored a record number of tries for England. How many?

190. As a youngster playing for Middlesbrough Rugby Club Rory Underwood played alongside which future England teammate?

ANDREW JOHNS

191. In what Australian state was Andrew Johns born?

192. In what position was Andrew Johns regarded as being the world's best for a number of years?

193. What English Rugby League club did Andrew Johns join in August 2005?

194. What career threatening injury did Andrew Johns experience in 2003?

195. How many caps did Andrew Johns win with Australia - 21,31 or 41?

196. At which Australian Rugby League club did Andrew Johns spend most of his career?

197. Against which club did Andrew Johns play his last game before being forced into retirement with a neck injury?

198. In 2007 The Wallabies Rugby Union authorities hired Andrew Johns in what capacity?

199. Why, on 26 August 2007, was Andrew Johns arrested in London?

200. Andrew Johns won the Player of the Series award for Australia against Great Britain in what year?

GAVIN HASTINGS

201. What is Gavin Hastings' full name?

202. In which city was Gavin Hastings born?

203. What is Gavin Hastings' nickname?

204. What is the name of Gavin Hastings' Scotland international brother?

205. In what position did Gavin Hastings play?

206. What honour has Gavin Hastings been awarded by the Queen?

207. Against which nation did both Hastings brothers make their Scotland debut in 1986?

208. What university did Gavin Hastings attend and play rugby for?

209. Gavin Hastings is the all-time highest point scorer for Scotland and the British and Irish Lions. How many points has he scored for both in total - A: 711, B: 722, C: 733, or D: 744?

210. In what year did Gavin Hastings win the Grand Slam with Scotland?

THE SPRINGBOKS

211. What colour is The Springboks' change kit shirts?

212. What is the name of the Springbok player who holds the record for most caps and top points scorer as of 2007?

213. Against which nation did South Africa achieve its biggest victory in 2005 (134-3)?

214. Against which nation did South Africa go down to its biggest defeat (53-3) in 2002?

215. In which two years has South Africa won the World Cup?

216. Who was the South African captain in 2007?

217. Who was South Africa coach in during the World Cup of 2007?

218. What was the score when South Africa played England in Pool A of the 2007 World Cup?

219. South Africa competes in the Tri-Nations Tournament with which other two countries?

220. Which nation had played 12 internationals against South Africa by the end of 2007 and won none of them?

MURRAYFIELD STADIUM

221. In which Scottish city is Murrayfield?

222. In what year was Murrayfield opened?

223. What attraction is next door to Murrayfield Stadium?

224. What is the nearest railway station to Murrayfield Stadium?

225. What is the capacity of Murrayfield Stadium?

226. Who is the architect responsible for Murrayfield Stadium?

227. To the nearest million, how much did the reconstruction of Murrayfield Stadium cost when it was completed in 1995?

228. Murrayfield hosted the Heineken Cup final of 2004-05. Which two clubs contested the match?

229. Which soccer club played its European matches at Murrayfield Stadium?

230. Murrayfield held a record attendance (104,000) in 1975 when Scotland played which nation?

SIR CLIVE WOODWARD

231. In what county was Sir Clive Woodward born?

232. For which club did Sir Clive Woodward play in 1974?

233. For which club did Sir Clive Woodward play between 1979 and 1985?

234. The young Clive Woodward was sent to HMS Conway School Ship as his father disapproved of his ambition to play which professional sport?

235. In what position did Sir Clive Woodward play for his club?

236. How many caps did Sir Clive Woodward win with the British and Irish Lions - A: 0, B: 1, C: 2, or D: 3?

237. In what year did Sir Clive Woodward become coach of the England rugby team?

238. At which soccer club did Sir Clive Woodward become Performance Director in 2005?

239. What was the title of Sir Clive Woodward's 2004 autobiography?

240. What degree did Sir Clive Woodward gain at Loughborough University?

MARTIN OFFIAH

241. In what year was Martin Offiah born?

242. Where was Martin Offiah born?

243. At which club did Martin Offiah begin his career?

244. What is Martin Offiah's nickname?

245. At which club did Martin Offiah make the most appearances and score the most points during his career?

246. In what year did Martin Offiah participate in the BBC's *Strictly Come Dancing* series?

247. How many times did Martin Offiah win the Rugby League Championship?

248. In what year was Martin Offiah awarded an MBE?

249. For which club did Martin Offiah play between 1996 and 1999?

250. A biography of Martin Offiah by David Lawrenson was published in 1993. What was its title?

HARLEQUINS

251. What was Harlequins Rugby League called prior to 2005?

252. What is the name of Harlequins' home ground?

253. What was the name of Harlequins when it was first formed in 1866?

254. Harlequins earned its present-day name in 1870, causing people who didn't like the new tag to split away. Which new club was formed as a result?

255. In what year did Harlequins win the John Player Cup?

256. Harlequins became the first British team to win what in 2001?

257. In what year was Harlequins relegated to National League One after finishing bottom of the Zurich Premiership?

258. In what year did Harlequins win the Powergen National Trophy?

259. What is the name of Harlequins' redeveloped West Stand?

260. Who was appointed Director of Rugby at Harlequins in 2005?

WALES

261. Who became Wales' coach in November 2007?

262. In what year did Wales play its first international match against England?

263. Against which nation did Wales record its biggest win in 2004?

264. Who is the man that was credited with introducing rugby to Wales in the 1850s?

265. The Welsh Rugby Union was formed on 12 March 1881 at the Castle Hotel in which town?

266. In 1972 Wales and which other nation refused to travel to Ireland to play due to threats allegedly from the IRA?

267. In which city did Wales play its first home international match?

268. Which is the only nation to have won the Six Nations title more times than Wales?

269. In what year did Wales reach the semi-finals of the Rugby Union World Cup?

270. Which player has scored the most points for Wales in his career?

ENGLISH RUGBY UNION LEAGUE CHAMPIONSHIP

271. In what year was the English Rugby Union League first contested?

272. Who was the first sponsor of the English Rugby Union League?

273. Which club won the first English Rugby Union Championship?

274. Which club won the 2006 Guinness Premiership?

275. Who was the sponsor of the Premiership when Newcastle Falcons won it for the first time in 1997-98?

276. Which two clubs have won the Premiership the most times?

277. Which club won the most Zurich Premiership titles?

278. When Leicester Tigers won the 2006-07 Guinness Premiership, which club finished top of the league?

279. In what season did Sky Sports first cover the English Rugby Union league?

280. Which team was relegated from the Guinness Premiership in 2006-07?

THE GRAND SLAM

281. What does a nation have to do to achieve the Grand Slam?

282. How many times has Ireland won the Grand Slam - A: 0, B:1, C: 2, or D: 3?

283. Which nation was the first to achieve the Grand Slam in 1908?

284. In what decade did France first win the Grand Slam?

285. In what decade did Scotland win its first post-Second World War Grand Slam?

286. How many times did Wales win the Grand Slam in the 1970s?

287. France won the Grand Slam in which two consecutive years of the 1990s?

288. As of 2007, how many times has Scotland won the Grand Slam?

289. Which nation won the Grand Slam three times in the 1990s?

290. Wales won the 2008 Grand Slam, but in what order did they defeat their opponents that year?

JONATHAN DAVIES

291. In which Welsh county was Jonathan Davies born?

292. In what year was Jonathan Davies born?

293. For which two Rugby Union clubs did Jonathan Davies play?

294. How many caps did Jonathan Davies win with Wales in Rugby Union - A: 12, B: 22, C: 32, or D: 42?

295. Which Rugby League club did Jonathan Davies join in 1989?

296. In what year was Jonathan Davies honoured with an MBE?

297. For which two Australian Rugby League clubs did Jonathan Davies play?

298. When Jonathan Davies returned to Rugby Union in 1995, which club did he join?

299. Jonathan Davies's wife Karen sadly passed away in what year?

300. What was Jonathan Davies' position in Rugby Union?

RUGBY LEAGUE WORLD CUP
1954-1960

301. In what nation was the 1954 Rugby League World Cup staged?

302. Which four nations took part in the 1954 Rugby League World Cup?

303. Which two nations drew 13-13 in the group stage of the 1954 Rugby League World Cup?

304. What nation hosted the 1957 Rugby League World Cup?

305. Which nation finished bottom of the 1957 Rugby League World Cup table?

306. Who won the 1957 Rugby League World Cup?

307. Which nation hosted the 1960 Rugby League World Cup?

308. Which city hosted the final match of the 1960 Rugby League World Cup?

309. Which nation won the 1960 Rugby League World Cup?

310. Which nation finished as runner-up in the 1960 Rugby League World Cup?

RAY GRAVELL

311. What is Ray Gravell's full name?

312. Where in Wales was Ray Gravell born?

313. What is Ray Gravell's nickname?

314. For what club did Ray Gravell play?

315. In what year did Ray Gravell make his international debut?

316. In what year did Ray Gravell play his last match for his club?

317. Ray Gravell was 'rugby consultant' and appeared as 'Referee No. 1' in which film?

318. In what film did Ray Gravell play Jeremy Irons' character's chauffeur?

319. In 1980 Ray Gravell made how many appearances for the British and Irish Lions?

320. Where, on 31 October 2007, did Ray Gravell sadly pass away?

MILLENNIUM STADIUM

321. What is the capacity of the Millennium Stadium?

322. In what year was the Millennium Stadium opened?

323. What is the name of the hawk that is employed to drive seagulls and pigeons out of the Millennium Stadium?

324. Which was the first soccer club to win the FA Cup at the Millennium Stadium?

325. Which club was the last to win a domestic cup soccer competition at the Millennium Stadium on 1 April 2007, when it was the Johnstone's Paint Trophy?

326. In what year did the Millennium Stadium host its first motor sport competition and what event was it?

327. True or false: the BBC Wales production of the Doctor Who episode 'Dalek' was primarily filmed at the Millennium Stadium?

328. Which two soccer clubs contested the first FA Cup final to be played indoors when the Millennium Stadium roof was closed for the event in 2003?

329. Which nation did the Welsh rugby team first play at the Millennium Stadium?

330. In what year did the Millennium Stadium first host the final of the Heineken Cup?

DAVID CAMPESE

331. What is David Campese's middle name?

332. In what year was David Campese born?

333. In what two positions did David Campese play?

334. What was David Campese's original career - A: laywer, B: cleaner, C: teacher, or D: hairdresser?

335. Where in Australia was David Campese born?

336. What is David Campese's nickname?

337. Against which nation did David Campese make his international debut?

338. David Campese made his last appearance for Australia in 1996 against which nation?

339. In what tournament did David Campese break the world record for tries scored?

340. Campese himself rates the 1984 Grand Slam series as one of his three finest tours. Who was Wallabies' coach?

LAWRENCE DALLAGLIO

341. In what year was Lawrence Dallaglio born?

342. What is Lawrence Dallaglio's middle name?

343. For what club did Lawrence Dallaglio play?

344. Against which nation did Lawrence Dallaglio make his Test debut?

345. In what position did Lawrence Dallaglio play?

346. What honour was Lawrence Dallaglio awarded by the Queen in 2004?

347. Lawrence Dallaglio's sister, Francesca, was a victim of what London disaster in 1989?

348. In what year did Lawrence Dallaglio first retire from international rugby?

349. Because of his parentage, Lawrence Dallaglio could have played for two other rugby nations. Which ones?

350. Lawrence Dallaglio was a member of the inaugural World Cup Sevens winning England squad. In what year was that?

BILL McLAREN

351. In what year was Bill McLaren born?

352. Where in Scotland was Bill McLaren born?

353. With military division did Bill McLaren serve during the Second World War?

354. Bill McLaren was on the verge of a full international Scottish cap in 1947 when he contracted which disease?

355. When Bill McLaren was a teacher, what subject did he teach?

356. In what year did Bill McLaren make his debut as a commentator on BBC radio?

357. Who was Scotland playing when Bill McLaren made his BBC radio commentating debut - A: England, B: Ireland, C: France, or D: Wales?

358. In what year did Bill McLaren make his debut on television?

359. Which soccer team does Bill McLaren support?

360. In what year did Bill McLaren hang up his microphone and retire?

RUGBY SCHOOL

361. In what decade was Rugby School founded?

362. What is the name of the founder of Rugby School - A: Laurence Hood, B: Laurence Sheriff, C: Laurence Scarlett, or D: Laurence Littlejohn?

363. In what English county does Rugby School reside?

364. The founder of Rugby School made his fortune by supplying groceries to which English Queen?

365. To what religious affiliation is Rugby School attached?

366. What is the current age range of pupils at Rugby School - A: 9-16, B; 9-18, C: 11-18, or D: 9-18?

367. According to Rugby School slang, to what does the word 'beak' refer - A: teacher, B: first year student, C: prefect, or D: Dunce?

368. Which of the following did not attend Rugby School - A: Salman Rushdie, B Lawrence Llewelyn-Bowen, C: Neville Chamberlain, or D: Lewis Carroll?

369. In what year were girls first admitted into the sixth form at Rugby School - A: 1970, B: 1975, C: 1980, or D: 1985.

370. Which of the Rugby School houses is featured in the book *Tom Brown's Schooldays* by Thomas Hughes - A: Cotton House, B: Griffin House, C: Whitelaw House, or D: School House.

ST HELENS

371. What are the basic features of the St Helens RLFC crest?

372. What is the name of St Helens' home ground?

373. In what year was St Helens founded - A: 1853, B: 1863, C: 1873, or D: 1883?

374. In 1977-78 St Helens lost in the final of the BBC2 Floodlit Trophy to which side?

375. What is the colour of St Helens' kit?

376. Which St Helens coach won the BBC Sports Personality Coach of the Year award in 2006?

377. Who was the captain that led St Helens to grand final success against Bradford in 1999?

378. What is the nearest city to St Helens?

379. What is the colour of St Helens' away shirts?

380. Which player made the most appearances for St Helens between 1961 and 1976?

RUGBY LEAGUE POSITIONS

381. In what position would a player wearing a number 8 shirt play in Rugby League?

382. What numbers would the wingers wear in Rugby League?

383. What number shirt would a prop forward (right) wear in Rugby League?

384. In what position would a player wearing a number 3 shirt play in Rugby League?

385. What number shirt would a fullback wear in Rugby League?

386. In what position would a player wearing a number 12 shirt play in Rugby League?

387. In what position would a player wearing a number 13 shirt play in Rugby League?

388. What number shirt would the hooker wear in Rugby League?

389. In what position would a player wearing a number 7 shirt play in Rugby League?

390. The stand-off/five-eight would wear what number shirt in Rugby League?

J.P.R. WILLIAMS

391. Where was J.P.R. Williams born?

392. In what decade was J.P.R. Williams born?

393. What was J.P.R. Williams' profession outside rugby?

394. What do the letters J.P.R. stand for in Williams' name?

395. In what year did J.P.R. Williams make his debut for Wales?

396. At which sport did J.P.R. Williams win a British Junior title in the sixties?

397. True or false: J.P.R. Williams' brother J.J. also played for Wales?

398. Name one of the two clubs that J.P.R. Williams played for.

399. How many caps did J.P.R .Williams win with Wales - A: 35, B: 45, C: 55, or D: 65?

400. J.P.R. Williams is best known for playing in what position?

RUGBY LEAGUE
WORLD CUP 1968-1970

401.   Who staged the 1968 Rugby League World Cup?

402.   Which was the only nation that Great Britain defeated in the 1968 Rugby League World Cup?

403.   At what stadium was the 1968 Rugby League World Cup final played?

404.   What nation did Australia defeat in the 1968 Rugby League World Cup final?

405.   When Australia beat France 37-4 in the 1968 Rugby League World Cup, in which city was the match played?

406.   What nation staged the 1970 Rugby League World Cup?

407.   Which nation was undefeated during the group stage of the 1970 Rugby League World Cup?

408.   Which city staged the 1970 Rugby League World Cup final?

409.   Which nation did France beat 17-15 in the final group game   of the 1970 Rugby League World Cup?

410.   Which nation finished bottom of the group stage of the 1970 Rugby League World Cup?

CALCUTTA CUP

411. In what year was the Calcutta Cup first contested?

412. How many players were there per team when the first Calcutta Cup match was contested?

413. Which two players were given bans after their antics resulted in the Calcutta Cup getting damaged in 1988?

414. Which player holds the record for scoring the most points in Calcutta Cup history?

415. Who won the Calcutta Cup in 1982 and in 1989?

416. Where was the Calcutta Cup held in Scotland prior to Scotland home games being held at Murrayfield?

417. In what decade was the last 0-0 draw between Scotland and England in the Calcutta Cup?

418. What was the score when Scotland beat England in the 2006 Calcutta Cup?

419. True of false: England won every Calcutta Cup of the 1990s?

420. True or false: England beat Scotland 15-0 at Murrayfield in 1978?

ELLERY HANLEY

421. In what year was Ellery Hanley born?

422. What was Ellery Hanley's nickname?

423. In which English city was Ellery Hanley born?

424. Ellery Hanley is best known for playing in what position?

425. At which club did Ellery Hanley make his first class debut in 1978?

426. What is the last English club for which Ellery Hanley served in the 1990s?

427. In what year was Ellery Hanley honoured by the Queen with an MBE?

428. How much did Wigan have to pay for Ellery Hanley's services when they signed him in 1985?

429. What number shirt did Ellery Hanley wear?

430. At which Australian club did Ellery Hanley finish his career?

TRIPLE CROWN

431. As of 2007, which is the most recent side to have achieved the Triple Crown?

432. As no trophy is awarded for the winners of the Triple Crown, what is its nickname?

433. Which nation has won the most Triple Crowns?

434. Which nation's last Triple Crown win of the 20th century was in 1990?

435. What nation first won the Triple Crown in consecutive years after 1947?

436. Which nation won the Triple Crown in four consecutive years of the 1970s?

437. True or false: England failed to win any Triple Crowns in the 1980s?

438. True of false: Wales was the only nation to achieve the Triple Crown between 1965 and 1979?

439. What was the last nation to achieve the Triple Crown before the Second World War began?

440. England achieved the Triple Crown in 1892, but when did it next achieve the feat - A: 1911, B: 1912, C: 1913, or D: 1914?

WARRINGTON

441. In what county does Warrington reside?

442. What is Warrington's nickname?

443. What are Warrington's club colours?

444. In what decade was Warrington RLFC founded?

445. What is the name of Warrington's home ground?

446. What was the name of Warrington's home ground before they moved?

447. In what season did Warrington first win the Championship?

448. Who became chairman of Warrington in 1999?

449. In 2000 Warrington recorded its biggest win (84-1) against which club?

450. In which season of the 1970s did Warrington win the Challenge Cup?

PARC DES PRINCES

451. What is the English translation of Parc des Princes?

452. What soccer team plays its home games at Parc des Princes?

453. In what year was Parc des Princes built - A: 1887, B: 1897, C: 1907, or D: 1917?

454. What was Parc des Princes originally used as?

455. Who owns the Parc des Princes - A: the French nation, B: the city of Paris, C: the French Rugby Union, or D: the French FA?

456. What year's Olympic Games were held at the Parc des Princes?

457. Matches from how many Rugby World Cup final tournaments have been held at Parc des Princes?

458. In what year was Parc des Princes replaced as the French National Stadium by Stade de France?

459. Which rugby club sometimes uses the Parc des Princes?

460. What is the capacity of Parc des Princes - A: 45,712, B: 46,712, C: 47,712, or D: 48,712?

FRIK DU-PREEZ

461. For what nation did Frik Du-Preez play?

462. In what year did Frik Du-Preez make his international debut?

463. In what position did Frik Du-Preez play?

464. In what decade was Frik Du-Preez born?

465. For what club did Frik Du-Preez play?

466. Against which nation did Frik Du-Preez make his last international appearance?

467. Against whom did Frik Du-Preez score his one international try?

468. When the Rugby Hall of Fame came into being in 1997, Frik du Preez was voted into it along with which other fellow countryman?

469. Where was Frik du Preez born?

470. Frik du Preez scored one conversion in his international career, against which nation?

ANDY FARRELL

471. Where was Andy Farrell born?

472. In what year's New Year's Honours was Andy Farrell awarded the OBE?

473. In what year was Andy Farrell born?

474. In what year did Andy Farrell make his debut for Great Britain against New Zealand?

475. In what year did Andy Farrell win the Golden Boot as the best Rugby League player in the world?

476. At which club did Andy Farrell play his entire Rugby League career?

477. Which Rugby Union club did Andy Farrell join in 2005?

478. Andy Farrell made a try-scoring Rugby Union debut against which club?

479. In what position was Andy Farrell playing when he made his debut for England against Scotland?

480. In what unfamiliar position was Andy Farrell made to play in England's first 2007 World Cup match against South Africa?

JASON LEONARD

481.   In what year was Jason Leonard born?

482.   Where was Jason Leonard born?

483.   In what position did Jason Leonard play?

484.   For what club did Jason Leonard first play first class
       rugby?

485.   How many times did Jason Leonard play for England?

486.   Which player surpassed Jason Leonard's record for
       international appearances in 2005?

487.   In what year did Jason Leonard first play for England?

488.   What nickname was given to Jason Leonard by Martin
       Bayfield, the former England second row?

489.   What career did Jason Leonard have before taking up
       rugby?

490.   At what club did Jason Leonard finish his rugby career?

BRADFORD BULLS

491. By what name was Bradford Bulls Rugby League club known prior to 1996?

492. In what year was Bradford Bulls founded?

493. What is the name of Bradford Bulls' home ground?

494. In what year did Bradford Northern first play at the current home ground?

495. Prior to 2000 in what season did Bradford Northern win win the Challenge Cup?

496. In what season did Bradford Northern win the Rugby League Premiership?

497. Who was chairman of Bradford Bulls in 2007?

498. What name is given to the event that led to the formation of   Bradford Northern Rugby League Club and Bradford City AFC?

499. In what year did Bradford Northern go out of business prior to being re-formed?

500. Who became Bradford Bulls' captain in 2007?

JONAH LOMU

501. In what year was Jonah Lomu born?

502. For which British Club has Jonah Lomu played?

503. What was Jonah Lomu's best position on the rugby field?

504. In what year did Jonah Lomu make his debut for New Zealand?

505. What medal did Jonah Lomu win with New Zealand at the 1998 Commonwealth Games in Kuala Lumpur?

506. Of which body organ did Jonah Lomu have a rare disorder resulting in a transplant in 2004?

507. What national honour was Jonah Lomu awarded in the Queen's birthday honours of 2007?

508. In what year did Jonah Lomu's international career end?

509. What Rugby World Cup record does Jonah Lomu hold?

510. Against which nation did Jonah Lomu make his international debut?

GAVIN HENSON

511.   Where in Wales was Gavin Henson born?

512.   Name one of the three rugby positions Gavin Henson is known to play in.

513.   What is Gavin Henson's middle name?

514.   For which club did Gavin Henson start playing in 2003?

515.   In October 2005 Gavin Henson published a book and ended up having to apologise to his teammates for some of the comments it contained. What was the title of the book?

516.   What is the name of the baby that Gavin Henson had with singer, Charlotte Church?

517.   On what form of transport was Gavin Henson travelling when his rowdy behaviour resulted in his being charged by the police in December 2007?

518.   What rugby club did Gavin Henson join at the age of 18?

519.   In what year was Gavin Henson named as the International Rugby Board's Young Player of the Year?

520.   In what nation did Gavin Henson make his debut for Wales?

BILL BEAUMONT

521. In what decade was Bill Beaumont born?

522. Bill Beaumont is best known for playing in what position?

523. In what year did Bill Beaumont make his debut for England?

524. Bill Beaumont came in as a late replacement for which player when he made his England debut?

525. Bill Beaumont has a rather unusual middle name. Is it - A: Smallridge, B: Whiteledge, C: Redridge, or D: Blackledge?

526. Where in Lancashire was Bill Beaumont born?

527. In what year did Bill Beaumont become England captain?

528. Bill Beaumont was captain of which year's Lions tour to South Africa?

529. Of which rugby charity is Bill Beaumont Honourary President?

530. In what year did Bill Beaumont finish his stint as a team captain on the BBC's *A Question of Sport*?

CHRIS PATERSON

531. In which city was Chris Paterson born?

532. Name one of the three positions that Chris Paterson plays in.

533. What is Chris Paterson's nickname?

534. What English club did Chris Paterson join in 2007?

535. On 13 November 2004 in the Scotland v. Japan game Chris Paterson's total points scored exceeded that of which Scotland legend?

536. In what year did Chris Paterson make his debut for Scotland?

537. On 27 November 2004 Chris Paterson became the youngest ever Scottish player to do what, aged 26?

538. For which club did Chris Paterson play between 1999 and 2007?

539. In 2007 Chris Paterson's Scotland scoring record was second only to which Scotland legend?

540. Chris Paterson was dropped for Scotland's opening Six Nations game of 2008 against France in favour of which Scottish kicker?

GILBERT

541. In what decade did Gilbert begin manufacturing sports products?

542. Who founded Gilbert?

543. In what year did the man who founded Gilbert sadly pass away - A: 1877, B: 1887, C: 1897, or D: 1907?

544. Where was the original Gilbert shop situated?

545. Which company acquired Gilbert in 2002?

546. What material was at the core of the original rugby balls manufactured by Gilbert and encased by leather?

547. In what year did the Gilbert family sell the business - A: 1938, B: 1958, C: 1978, or D: 1998?

548. At what year's tournament was the Gilbert first adopted as the ball of the World Cup?

549. What was the name of the last Gilbert family member to be involved in the company?

550. True or false: Gilbert made the ball that William Webb-Ellis ran with in 1823?

RUGBY LEAGUE WORLD CUP 1972

551.   Which nation staged the 1972 Rugby League World Cup?

552.   Who did Great Britain defeat 53-19 in the 1972 Rugby League World Cup?

553.   Which nation finished second bottom of the group stage of the 1972 Rugby League World Cup table?

554.   Which was the only nation to be defeated by France during the 1972 Rugby League World Cup?

555.   What was unusual about the final score of the 1972 Rugby League World Cup?

556.   What city staged the final of the 1972 Rugby League World Cup?

557.   True or false: Great Britain played one game of the 1972 Rugby League World Cup at the Parc de Princes, Paris?

558.   The losing finalist of the 1972 Rugby League World Cup had already lost to the eventual winner of the trophy in the group stage. Who was the runner-up?

559.   What is the name of the stadium that staged the 1972 Rugby League World Cup final - A: Stade De Gerland, B: Patinoire Charlemagne, C: Vuillermet, or D: Stade de La Duchère?

560.   What was the attendance of the 1972 Rugby League World Cup final - A: 45, B: 450, C: 4,500, or D: 45,000?

NIGEL STARMER-SMITH

561. In what decade was Nigel Starmer-Smith born?

562. In what position did Nigel Starmer-Smith play?

563. For what first class club did Nigel Starmer-Smith play?

564. What was Nigel Starmer-Smith's career outside rugby while he was still playing?

565. How many England caps did Nigel Starmer-Smith earn - A: 2, B: 7, C: 12, or D: 17?

566. Of what magazine was Nigel Starmer-Smith the editor?

567. What BBC series did Nigel Starmer-Smith present for 15 years?

568. In what year did Nigel Starmer-Smith earn his first England cap?

569. What Olympic sport did Nigel Starmer-Smith commentate on for the BBC in 1988?

570. True of false: during the 2003 Rugby World Cup, Nigel Starmer-Smith commentated for ITV Sport?

BRYAN HABANA

571. Name one of Bryan Habana's four best known nicknames.

572. From which sportsman did Bryan Habana get his first name?

573. In what year was Bryan Habana born?

574. Bryan Habana is best known for playing in what position?

575. In what year did Bryan Habana make his debut for South Africa?

576. How many tries did Bryan Habana score in the 2007 Rugby World Cup?

577. What South African Super Rugby club did Bryan Habana join in 2005?

578. Bryan Habana's middle name is Gary, named after which former sportsman?

579. In what year did Bryan Habana win the IRB Player of the Year award?

580. What species of animal did Bryan Habana once race for charity?

CASTLEFORD TIGERS

581. In which county is Castleford located?

582. What is the name of Castleford's home ground?

583. In what decade was Castleford founded?

584. What was the old name for Castleford's home ground?

585. In what season was the word 'Tigers' added to Castleford's name?

586. What retail chain bought Castleford Tigers?

587. What is the name of Castleford Tigers' chairman?

588. Castleford Tigers' biggest win was 106-0 against whom in 2007?

589. Castleford Tigers' biggest Super League defeat was 4-72 against whom in 2006?

590. Which Castleford Tigers player scored 244 points in 1999?

RUGBY UNION POSITIONS

591. In what position would a Rugby Union player wearing a number 1 shirt play?

592. What number shirt would a hooker wear in Rugby Union?

593. In what position would a player wearing a number 12 shirt play in Rugby Union?

594. What number shirt would a tighthead prop wear in Rugby Union?

595. What is the name of the position that the player wearing a number 8 shirt plays in Rugby Union?

596. What number shirts do the two locks wear in Rugby Union?

597. What is the name of the position that a player wearing a number 7 shirt plays in Rugby Union?

598. A Rugby Union player wearing a number 14 shirt plays in what position?

599. What number shirt does a fly half wear in Rugby Union?

600. 15 is the shirt number associated with what Rugby Union position?

PHIL VICKERY

601. In what year was Phil Vickery born?

602. What was Phil Vickery's first job - A: policeman, B: postman, C: clergyman, or D: milkman?

603. Who did Phil Vickery replace as England captain?

604. In what county was Phil Vickery born?

605. In what position does Phil Vickery play?

606. For what club did Phil Vickery play for eleven years?

607. What club did Phil Vickery join in 2006?

608. What is Phil Vickery's nickname?

609. In what year did Phil Vickery make his England debut?

610. What is Phil Vickery's middle name - A: John, B: Paul, C: George, or D: Richard?

FRANCE RUGBY UNION TEAM

611. What is the nickname of the French team?

612. What is the emblem of the French team?

613. Which French player has won the most caps (118) during his career?

614. Which French player has scored the most tries (38) during his career?

615. Who became the French national coach in 2007?

616. Who became the captain of France in 2008?

617. Which player has scored the most points for France in his career?

618. Against which nation did France play its first international match in 1906 - A: Scotland, B: Australia, C: New Zealand, or D: England?

619. France's biggest win was in 1974 against which nation - A: Argentina, B: Chile, C: Brazil, or D: Peru?

620. What is the lowest stage of the World Cup that France has achieved in every tournament up to and including 2007?

HULL FC

621. In what year was Hull FC formed - A: 1865, B: 1866, C: 1867, or D: 1868?

622. What are Hull's nicknames?

623. What is the name of Hull FC's home ground?

624. What song has been considered as the battle cry of Hull fans since the 1930s?

625. Hull FC was the last winner of which trophy in 1980?

626. In what season did Hull FC first win the Championship?

627. What player scored 250 tries in two spells with Hull FC between 1961 and 1974 and also 1981 and 1985?

628. What team did Hull FC beat 88-0 in March 2003?

629. Which team defeated Hull FC 71-0 in the 2005 play-offs?

630. What was the last season that Hull FC won the Championship?

SUPER LEAGUE

631. In what year was the Super League founded?

632. Who approached European clubs with a mind to form the Super League?

633. What was the French team that featured in the first season of the Super League?

634. Several mergers were suggested when the Super League was being formed. What was the proposed name if Warrington and Widnes had been joined together?

635. The Super League was inspired by a similar competition in which country?

636. To what division would a Super League club be relegated?

637. What team was promoted to the Super League in 2007?

638. What team was promoted to the Super League in 2006?

639. In what year were promotion and relegation reintroduced in the Super League?

640. In what year was Leigh Centurions relegated from the Super League?

NATIONAL LEAGUE CLUB
HOME GROUNDS

641. What club plays its home games at Boundary Park?

642. What former Super League club plays its home games at the Willows?

643. What former Super League club plays its home games at the Don Valley Stadium?

644. What former Super League club plays its home games at the Stobart Stadium Halton?

645. What former Super League club plays its home games at Hilton Park?

646. What club plays its home games at Mount Pleasant?

647. What club plays its home games at Post Office Road?

648. What club plays its home games at Brewery Field?

649. What club plays its home games at The Shay?

650. What club plays its home games at The Tetley's Stadium?

THE NATIONAL LEAGUE

651. What is the name of the Welsh Rugby League team in National League?

652. How would a team earn one point in the National League?

653. Who sponsors the National League as of 2008?

654. What was the name of the competition that ran prior to its reorganisation into the National League?

655. In what year was the National League formed?

656. When Blackpool Panthers was elected into National League Two in 2005, which defunct club did it replace?

657. Between what years did National League Three run?

658. What is the name of the National League side from London?

659. Which two clubs were relegated from National League One in 2007?

660. Which club won the first National League One title?

SIX NATIONS CHAMPIONSHIPS

661. In what decade was the inaugural Home Nations
     Rugby Championship (England, Ireland, Scotland and
     Wales) first contested?

662. In what year did Wales first win the Home Nations
     Championship?

663. In what year did France officially join the competition,
     coining its new name, The Five Nations Championship?

664. In what year was France ejected from the Five Nations
     Championship?

665. Wales played its home games for the 2008 Six Nations
     against which sides?

666. What is the name of the trophy contested between
     France and Italy?

667. In what year was the first actual trophy presented to
     the winners of the Five Nations?

668. In what year did Italy join the competition, giving
     birth to the Six Nations Championship?

669. Italy won its opening Six Nations game against the
     reigning champions - who?

670. What event disrupted the Six Nations Championship of
     2001, with some matches being postponed until the
     autumn?

WRU CHALLENGE CUP

671. In what year was the first WRU Challenge Cup final played?

672. Who was the inaugural winner of the WRU Challenge Cup?

673. Which club won the WRU Challenge Cup for the first time when it beat Cardiff 20-18 in 2007?

674. Which club won the WRU Challenge Cup four consecutive times in the 1970s?

675. Which club won its one and only WRU Challenge Cup in 1983 when it beat Swansea 18-6?

676. Which club has won the most WRU Challenge Cups?

677. Which team did Neath beat 36-13 in the 2004 WRU Challenge Cup final?

678. In 1982 Cardiff and Bridgend drew 12-12. How did Cardiff win the WRU Challenge Cup?

679. Which club did Swansea beat 37-10 in the 1999 WRU Challenge Cup final?

680. Which club won the WRU Challenge Cup in 1977 and in 2001?

LLANELLI RFC

681. What is the colour of Llanelli's away shirts?

682. In what decade was Llanelli founded?

683. What is the name of Llanelli's home ground?

684. What is Llanelli's colour-related nickname?

685. The Max Boyce song 'The Day the Pubs Ran Dry' refers to the aftermath of a 1972 encounter between Llanelli and which team?

686. Sosban Fach is a nickname for Llanelli, but what is the English translation?

687. What is traditionally put on top of the posts when Llanelli plays Bath, which the winning team keeps until their next encounter?

688. What father and son combination has played for Llanelli and Wales?

689. How many times did Llanelli win the WRU Challenge Cup in the 1990s?

690. In what season did Llanelli first win the Welsh Premier Division?

RUGBY LEAGUE WORLD CUP
1975

691. Two new nations took part in the 1975 Rugby League World Cup, but which ones?

692. Where in Wales was the only 1975 Rugby League World Cup tie to be played in that nation?

693. France won just one of its 1975 Rugby League World Cup ties, against whom?

694. England played out a 17-17 draw against which nation in the 1975 Rugby League World Cup?

695. Which stadium staged the 1975 Rugby League World Cup final?

696. Which nation did England defeat 48-2 in the 1975 Rugby League World Cup?

697. What was the only nation to defeat Australia during the group stage of the 1975 Rugby League World Cup?

698. Which New Zealand stadium staged three 1975 Rugby League World Cup ties?

699. Wales travelled to Sydney to play Australia in the 1975 Rubgy League World Cup. What stadium staged the tie?

700. Which nation won the 1975 World Cup by 25-0?

HUDDERSFIELD GIANTS

701. In what decade was the Huddersfield Athletic Club formed?

702. What year is featured on the Huddersfield Giants' logo?

703. What, apart from 'Giants', is the nickname of Huddersfield?

704. Where do Huddersfield Giants play their home games?

705. What are the Huddersfield club colours?

706. Who became Huddersfield Giants' coach in 2003?

707. In what decade did Huddersfield last win the Challenge Cup?

708. Huddersfield's biggest win was 142-4 against which club?

709. In what decade did Huddersfield last win the Rugby League Championship?

710. Which club did Huddersfield Giants merge with in 1999?

ANDY IRVINE

711. Andy Irvine was born in what decade?

712. In what year did Andy Irvine make his debut for Scotland?

713. Andy Irvine is best known for playing in what position?

714. What is Andy Irvine's middle name - A: Hartley, B: Branstone, C: Robertson, or D: Sharwood?

715. Andy Irvine is a former President of what?

716. During what year's Easter tour did Andy Irvine play for the Barbarians - A: 1975, B: 1976, C: 1977, or D: 1978?

717. What was Andy Irvine's career outside rugby while he was still playing - A: chartered surveyor, B: chartered accountant, C: insurance rep., or D: taxman?

718. Andy Irvine played his club rugby where?

719. What award has Andy Irvine received from the Queen?

720. In what year did Andy Irvine play his last game for Scotland?

LESLEY VAINIKOLO

721. In what year was Lesley Vainikolo born?

722. In what nation was Lesley Vainikolo born?

723. Lesley Vainikolo is best known by two nicknames - King Lesley and what else?

724. For which Rugby League nation is Lesley Vainikolo an international?

725. For which Rugby League club did Lesley Vainikolo play?

726. In what position does Lesley Vainikolo play?

727. Which Union club did Lesley Vainikolo join when he changed codes in 2007?

728. Against which nation did Lesley Vainikolo make his Rugby Union international debut for England?

729. For what Australian Rugby League club did Lesley Vainikolo play?

730. Against which club did Lesley Vainikolo make his last Super League appearance?

WAKEFIELD TRINITY WILDCATS

731. In what decade was Wakefield Trinity formed?

732. In what year did Wakefield Trinity Wildcats win promotion to the Super League?

733. What is the name of Wakefield Trinity Wildcats' home ground?

734. Wakefield's final game of the 2001 season was a relegation battle with Salford City Reds, with Wakefield condemning which club to relegation?

735. Whom did Wakefield Trinity Wildcats sack in June 2005 after a disappointing start to the season?

736. The Wildcats defeated their arch-rivals by 29-17 at home on Saturday 16 September 2006 to preserve their Super League status. Which club was that?

737. In November 2006 Wakefield City Council set out plans for a new sporting village to be built, which would incorporate a new stadium for the Wildcats' use. Where?

738. Wakefield Trinity won the Rugby League championship in two consecutive seasons. When?

739. When, in the 1960s, did Wakefield Trinity last win the Challenge Cup?

740. Which Wakefield Trinity Wildcats player set a record for most points in a match (36) versus Chorley in 2004?

WILL CARLING

741. In what year was Will Carling born - A: 1964, B: 1965, C: 1966, or D: 1967?

742. In what year did Will Carling earn his England debut against France in Paris?

743. What was Will Carling's career outside of rugby while he was playing?

744. For what club did Will Carling play?

745. Will Carling is best known for playing in what position?

746. What public figure was Will Carling romantically linked with by the press?

747. Will Carling was the youngest ever England captain at what age?

748. Will Carling is often known in Rugby Union circles by what nickname?

749. Will Carling was once married to which TV presenter?

750. How many England caps did Will Carling earn - A: 52, B: 62, C: 72, or D: 82?

IRELAND

751. What is the emblem of the Irish Rugby Football Union?

752. What ground did Ireland adopt while Lansdowne Road was redeveloped?

753. Against which nation did Ireland fall to its biggest defeat in 1999?

754. True or false: Brian O'Driscoll is Ireland's most capped player as of 2007?

755. At which cricket ground did Ireland play its first international match against England in February 1875?

756. What is the furthest that Ireland has progressed in any World Cup tournament?

757. Which player has scored the most points for Ireland (as of 2008)?

758. Against which nation did Ireland achieve its largest winning margin in June 2000?

759. Who was the Ireland coach for the 2008 Six Nations?

760. Which Englishman was Ireland Head Coach between 1997 and 1998?

RUGBY LEAGUE WORLD CUP 1977 AND 1985-88

761. What stadium staged most of the 1977 Rugby League World Cup ties?

762. Which nation lost all three of its group games in the 1977 Rugby League World Cup?

763. Who scored a last-minute try to secure the 1977 Rugby League World Cup for Australia?

764. What was the final score of the 1977 Rugby League World Cup final?

765. Which city staged just one 1977 Rugby League World Cup match between New Zealand and Great Britain?

766. What new nation took part in the 1985-88 Rugby League World Cup?

767. Which nation beat Australia 18-0 in the opening game of the 1985-88 Rugby League World Cup?

768. Which nation failed to fulfil two fixtures in the 1985-88 Rugby League World Cup?

769. Only one nation got to play all eight of its group games in the 1985-88 Rugby League World Cup. Which one?

770. Which nation did Australia defeat 25-12 in the 1985-88 Rugby League World Cup final?

DAN CARTER

771. In which region of New Zealand was Dan Carter born?

772. In what decade was Dan Carter born?

773. What is Dan Carter's nickname?

774. Dan Carter is best known for playing in what position?

775. In what year did Dan Carter make his debut for New Zealand?

776. In what year did Dan Carter win the IRB Player of the Year award?

777. Dan Carter scored 29 points against which nation in June 2007, an individual single-match record for an All Black?

778. For which club was Dan Carter playing when he made his international debut?

779. Dan Carter scored 60 points against which nation in 2006, the most by any player in a calendar year?

780. Against which home nation did Dan Carter make his international debut?

WIGAN WARRIORS

781.   What is the design of Wigan Warriors' home shirts?

782.   What appears on the red shield of the Wigan Warriors' crest - A: cannon, B: sword, C: jousting knight, or D: castle?

783.   In what decade was Wigan RLFC formed?

784.   What is the name of Wigan Warriors' home ground?

785.   Who became the coach of Wigan Warriors in 2006?

786.   Wigan Warriors was formerly owned by the owner of Wigan Football Club. What is his name?

787.   In what year did Wigan Warriors first win the Super League?

788.   Wigan Warriors' heaviest defeat was 75-0 in the Powergen Challenge Cup quarter-final against which club?

789.   In November 1999, which coach was sacked by Wigan chairman Maurice Lindsay after the Warriors' failure to win a trophy for the first time in 15 years?

790.   Wigan purchased whom from Bradford Bulls in 2006 for a staggering £470,000, making him the world's most expensive player?

RUGBY UNION WORLD CUP
1995

791. Which nation staged the 1995 World Cup?

792. As well as South Africa, what was the other African representative nation in the 1995 World Cup?

793. Which two nations competed in the Third Place match of the 1995 World Cup?

794. What is the name of the largest capacity stadium to be used in the 1995 World Cup?

795. Australia lost one of its pool matches 27-18 against which nation?

796. Whom did Italy beat 31-25 in the pool stage of the 1995 World Cup?

797. Which nation qualified along with New Zealand for the quarter-finals from Pool C in the 1995 World Cup?

798. Which French player was the top points scorer in the 1995 World Cup?

799. Which was the only home nation to fail to qualify for the 1995 World Cup quarter-finals?

800. Whom did South Africa defeat in the 1995 World Cup final?

JOE LYDON

801. In what decade was Joe Lydon born?

802. Joe Lydon played his first schoolboy curtain-raiser in the Challenge Cup final at Wembley in what year?

803. What professional Rugby League club did Joe Lydon first sign with on professional terms?

804. In what year did Joe Lydon make his full debut for Great Britain?

805. How much did Wigan have to pay to sign Joe Lydon - A: £50,000, B: £100,000, C: £150,000, or D: £200,000?

806. In what year did Joe Lydon win both the Lance Todd Trophy and the Man of Steel Award?

807. How many games did Joe Lydon play for Wigan - A: 232, B: 242, C: 252, or D: 262?

808. What post did Joe Lydon hold with the RFL from 1997 until 2000?

809. In 2007 Joe Lydon joined which Rugby Union club as Performance Consultant?

810. What job did Joe Lydon take up in 2004 with the England Rugby Union team?

SARACENS

811. In what year was Saracens founded - A: 1876, B: 1881, C: 1886, or D: 1891?

812. Where in England is Saracens based?

813. What is Saracens' nickname?

814. What is the name of Saracens' home ground?

815. In November 1995 Saracens gained the financial backing of whom, enabling the club to recruit some star players?

816. Who is the South African that became playing captain of Saracens in 2007?

817. Who was Saracens' club captain in 2007?

818. In what part of London was Saracens founded?

819. Saracens was the first English Premiership club to tour which nation?

820. Which Saracens player played for New Zealand in the 2007 World Cup?

WIDNES VIKINGS

821. What is the name of Widnes Vikings' home ground?

822. Which club is Widnes Vikings closest rival?

823. In what decade was Widnes Vikings founded?

824. What is Widnes Vikings' traditional nickname?

825. Who purchased Widnes Vikings after the club went into administration in 2007?

826. What was the name of Widnes RLFC when it was first formed?

827. How many times had Widnes won the Challenge Cup prior to the formation of the Super League - A: 7, B: 8, C: 9, or D: 10?

828. Which team defeated Widnes Vikings in the 2007 National League grand final?

829. Who became head coach of Widnes Vikings after the club's relegation from the Super League in 2005?

830. In what season did Widnes win the BBC2 Floodlit Trophy?

JEREMY GUSCOTT

831. In what year was Jeremy Guscott born - A: 1962, B: 1963, C: 1964, or D: 1965?

832. Jeremy Guscott played for the club from the city of his birth. Where was that?

833. What was Jeremy Guscott's original career outside rugby?

834. For which national plc did Jeremy Guscott work in a public relations role?

835. In what position did Jeremy Guscott play?

836. In what year did Jeremy Guscott make his debut for England?

837. Jeremy Guscott played his last game for England in the 1999 World Cup against which nation?

838. Jeremy Guscott marked his England debut with a hat-trick of tries in the 58-3 win over which European nation?

839. How many England caps did Jeremy Guscott earn in his career - A: 55, B: 65, C: 75, or D: 85?

840. Who employed Jeremy Guscott after he retired from rugby?

ITALY

841. In what decade did Italy play its first international?

842. Against which nation did Italy play its first international?

843. Italy achieved its biggest win in 1994 when it beat whom 104-8?

844. Against which nation did Italy crash to a 101-0 defeat in 1999?

845. What is the name of Italy's home ground?

846. What is the nickname of the Italian Rugby Union team?

847. Which South African became the coach of the Italian side in 2007?

848. Who was named captain of the Italian side for the 2008 Six Nations Championship?

849. Who was Italy's most capped player by the end of 2007?

850. Which two nations did Italy defeat in the 2007 Home Nations?

GREAT BRITAIN RUGBY LEAGUE

851. What is the predominant colour of Great Britain's home shirts?

852. What is the nickname of the Great Britain Rugby League team?

853. Against which nation did Great Britain play its first Rugby League match?

854. Against which nation did Great Britain achieve its biggest win in 1996?

855. In what year of the 2000s did Great Britain succumb to a 64-10 defeat to Australia?

856. Which Australian was appointed as full-time coach to the Great Britain Rugby League team in 2001?

857. What name is given to the series of matches between Great Britain and Australia?

858. Who departed as head coach of the Great Britain Rugby League team when his contract expired in 2006?

859. Who became head coach of the Great Britain Rugby League team in March 2007?

860. Who was the Samoan-born prop that was selected for the Great Britain Rugby League squad in 2007?

PAUL GRAYSON

861. In what year was Paul Grayson born?

862. In what English county was Paul Grayson born?

863. Paul Grayson is best known for playing in what position?

864. For which club did Paul Grayson play from 1997?

865. In what year did Paul Grayson make his debut for England?

866. Against which nation did Paul Grayson make his international debut - A: Western Samoa, B: Fiji, C: Italy, or D: Romania?

867. What is Paul Grayson's nickname?

868. How many England caps did Paul Grayson win - A: 12, B: 22, C: 32, or D: 42?

869. In what year did Paul Grayson play his last game for England?

870. How many hundred points did Paul Grayson score for England?

LEEDS RHINOS

871. In what decade was Leeds Rhinos founded?

872. In 2006 Leeds' home ground became known as the Headlingley _____ Stadium? (Fill in the blank)

873. Who became coach of Leeds Rhinos in December 2007?

874. What is the name of Leeds Rhinos' match-day mascot?

875. How many times has Leeds Rhinos won the World Club Challenge?

876. In what year did Leeds Rhinos first win the Super League?

877. When Leeds Rhinos won the Challenge Cup in 1999, how many times had they done it?

878. What is the predominant colour of Leeds Rhinos' home shirts?

879. Leeds Rhinos beat which team in the Super League grand final?

880. In 1921, which player became Rugby League's first £1,000 transfer when he moved from Hunslet to Leeds - A: Joe Wareham, B: Syd Hynes, C: Lewis Jones, or D: Harold Buck?

JON WEBB

881. In what year was Jon Webb born - A: 1960, B: 1961, C: 1962, or D: 1963?

882. In what English city was Jon Webb born - A: Manchester, B: London, C: Bristol, or D: Birmingham?

883. What is Jon Webb's nickname?

884. What university did Jon Webb attend - A: Bristol, B: Cardiff, C: Oxford, or D: Cambridge?

885. Jon Webb is best known for playing in what position?

886. For which two clubs did Jon Webb play?

887. In what year did Jon Webb first play for England?

888. In how many World Cups did Jon Webb represent England?

889. How many points did Jon Webb score for England - A: 296, B: 306, C: 316, or D: 326?

890. What career did Jon Webb take up after retiring from rugby?

RUGBY LEAGUE WORLD CUP
1989-1992

891. What stadium hosted the opening game of The Rugby League World Cup 1989-1992 - A: Wembley Stadium, B: Lloyd Robson Oval, Port Moresby, C: Lang Park, Brisbane, or D: Mount Smart Stadium, Auckland?

892. Which nation defeated France 34-0 in Carcassonne?

893. Which nation did France beat twice?

894. Which nation defeated Great Britain 14-0 in its opening game?

895. Which nation scored the most points (66) in one match against Papua New Guinea?

896. Which was the first English stadium to stage a Rugby League World Cup 1989-1992 game?

897. What stadium staged the game between Great Britain and France played on 7 March 1992?

898. In the last group match of the Rugby League World Cup 1989-1992, how many points did Papua New Guinea score against Australia - A: 6, B: 10, C: 14, or D: 18?

899. True or false: Australia was undefeated in the Rugby League World Cup 1989-1992?

900. Which stadium staged the Rugby League World Cup 1989- 1992 final?

ROB ANDREW

901. In what county was Rob Andrew born?

902. What is Rob Andrew's nickname?

903. Rob Andrew is best known for playing in what position?

904. In what other sport did Rob Andrew excel?

905. In how many Rugby World Cup tournaments did Rob Andrew play?

906. With which club did Rob Andrew win the English League in 1990?

907. Which England World Cup winner is Rob Andrew credited with discovering?

908. Which club did Rob Andrew join in 1995?

909. How many international caps did Rob Andrew win in his career - A: 51, B: 61, C: 71, or D: 81?

910. On 18 August 2006 Rob Andrew was appointed by the RFU to undertake which post?

LEICESTER TIGERS

911. In what decade was Leicester Tigers founded?

912. What is the name of Leicester Tigers' home ground?

913. When Leicester Tigers won the Guinness Premiership in
      2007, how many times had the team achieved that
      feat?

914. In what year did Leicester Tigers first win the
      Heineken Cup?

915. What is the name of Leicester Tigers' former
      Argentinian coach?

916. On 5 May 2007 Leicester Tigers beat which side in the
      Guinness Premiership play-off final?

917. True or false: Leicester Tigers once ground-shared
      Walkers Stadium with Leicester City FC?

918. What is the predominant colour of Leicester Tigers'
      home shirts?

919. Who was captain of Leicester Tigers at the beginning
      of 2008?

920. What was the nickname of Leicester Tigers' legendary
      coach Herbert Victor White?

BRIAN O'DRISCOLL

921. In what year was Brian O'Driscoll born?

922. What is Brian O'Driscoll's middle name - A: John, B: Seamus, C: Ronan, or D: Gerald?

923. Name Brian O'Driscoll's nicknames (a point for each).

924. For what Irish Rugby Union team did Brian O'Driscoll begin   playing in 1999?

925. In what year did Brian O'Driscoll make his debut for Ireland?

926. In what year did Brian O'Driscoll make his debut for the British and Irish Lions?

927. Brian O'Driscoll is best known for playing in what position?

928. In what year did Brian O'Driscoll become captain of Ireland?

929. In 2000 Brian O'Driscoll scored a hat-trick for Ireland when   it beat which nation for the first time in his lifetime?

930. In 2002 Brian O'Driscoll scored a hat-trick of tries when Ireland defeated which nation 43-22?

2008 SIX NATIONS

931. Who scored Italy's try in its opening defeat to Ireland in the 2008 Six Nations?

932. Who scored three penalties, one drop goal, and one conversion when England lost 26-19 to Wales in the 2008 Six Nations?

933. Who scored two tries for France when it beat Scotland 27-6 in the 2008 Six Nations?

934. Who scored all of Scotland's 15 points against Wales in the 2008 Six Nations?

935. Who scored most of Italy's points when it beat Scotland 23-20 in the 2008 Six Nations?

936. Who scored two tries for Ireland when it beat Scotland 34-13 in the 2008 Six Nations?

937. Who scored a hat-trick of tries for France against Ireland in the 2008 Six Nations?

938. Who scored most of England's points when it beat Ireland in the 2008 Six Nations?

939. Who was Ireland's top points scorer in the 2008 Six Nations?

940. Name the two Williams that scored Wales's tries in the Grand Slam decider against France in the 2008 Six Nations?

CHARLIE HODGSON

941. In what year was Charlie Hodgson born?

942. Where was Charlie Hodgson born?

943. For what club did Charlie Hodgson begin playing in 2000?

944. Charlie Hodgson is best known for playing in what position?

945. What is Charlie Hodgson's middle name - A: Christopher, B: Jonathon, C: Robert, or D: James?

946. In what year did Charlie Hodgson make his debut for England?

947. Whilst playing for England against South Africa on 18 November 2006, Charlie Hodgson ruptured what ligament in his right knee?

948. How many points did Charlie Hodgson score in his England debut against Romania - A: 22, B: 33, C: 44, or D: 55?

949. For what position was Charlie Hodgson selected for the 2003 Six Nations?

950. What university did Charlie Hodgson attend?

RUGBY LEAGUE WORLD CUP 1995

951.　What nation hosted the 1995 Rugby League World
　　　Cup?

952.　How many nations participated in the 1995 Rugby
　　　League World Cup?

953.　What was the only nation to defeat Australia in the
　　　1995 Rugby League World Cup?

954.　Name all of the nations that participated in the 1995
　　　Rugby League World Cup.

955.　Which nation only managed one victory in the 1995
　　　Rugby League World Cup?

956.　Which two nations drew their 1995 Rugby League
　　　World Cup encounter?

957.　Which four nations qualified for the 1995 Rugby
　　　League World Cup semi-finals?

958.　Which Australian player was the top points scorer in
　　　the 1995 Rugby League World Cup?

959.　One 1995 Rugby League World Cup semi-final was
　　　played at the McAlpine Stadium, Huddersfield, but
　　　where was the other one contested?

960.　Which nation won the 1995 Rugby League World Cup?

STACEY JONES

961. In what year was Stacey Jones born?

962. Stacey Jones is best known for playing in what position?

963. For what club did Stacey Jones play between 1995 and 2005?

964. What club did Stacey Jones join in 2006?

965. What is Stacey Jones' nickname?

966. In what year did Stacey Jones make his full debut for New Zealand?

967. What is the name of Stacey Jones' New Zealand international grandfather?

968. In what year did Stacey Jones retire as a player?

969. What club did Stacey Jones join as a goal-kicking coach?

970. In what year did Stacey Jones win the Golden Boot Award - World's Best Rugby League Player of the Year?

DUSTY HARE

971. In what decade was Dusty Hare born?

972. What is Dusty Hare's real first name?

973. For which nation did Dusty Hare play?

974. Dusty Hare is best known for playing in what position?

975. In which county was Dusty Hare born?

976. In what year did Dusty Hare make his international debut?

977. Against which nation did Dusty Hare make his international debut?

978. Against which nation did Dusty Hare make his last international appearance in 1984?

979. For which club did Dusty Hare play when he made his international debut?

980. What was Dusty Hare's career outside rugby while he was playing?

RUGBY UNION WORLD CUP 1999

981. Which nation hosted the 1999 Rugby Union World Cup?

982. Which player scored the most points in the 1999 Rugby Union World Cup?

983. Following on from question 982, what was the nationality of that player?

984. Which nation did Uruguay defeat 27-15 in the 1999 Rugby Union World Cup?

985. Which nation beat England 30-16 in Pool 2 of the 1999 Rugby Union World Cup?

986. Which nation did England defeat 101-10 in the 1999 Rugby Union World Cup?

987. Which nation did Canada beat 72-11 in Pool 3 of the 1999 Rugby Union World Cup?

988. Which nation qualified along with France from Pool 3 in the 1999 Rugby Union World Cup?

989. Only one nation failed to qualify from Pool 4 of the 1999 Rugby Union World Cup. Which one?

990. Which nation knocked England out of the 1999 Rugby Union World Cup?

WILL GREENWOOD

991.   In what year was Will Greenwood born?

992.   In what county was Will Greenwood born?

993.   Will Greenwood's father was also an England international. What is his first name?

994.   Will Greenwood is best known for playing in what position?

995.   With what club did Will Greenwood have two spells during his career?

996.   For what club did Will Greenwood play from 1996 to 2000?

997.   In what year did Will Greenwood make his full England debut?

998.   Will Greenwood won his 50th England cap in the 2004 Six Nations against whom?

999.   In what year did Will Greenwood retire from rugby?

1000. How many British and Irish Lions caps did Will Greenwood earn - A: 3, B: 4, C: 5, or D: 6?

LANCE TODD TROPHY

1001. For what is the Lance Todd Trophy awarded?

1002. Which future Rugby Union World Cup winner was awarded the Lance Todd Trophy in 1995?

1003. In 2007 which two players shared the Lance Todd Trophy?

1004. Which player won the first Lance Todd Trophy in 1946 - A: Ernest Ward, B: Frank Whitcombe, C: Willie Davies, or D: Billy Stott?

1005. Which player won the Lance Todd Trophy twice during the 1990s?

1006. What nationality was Lance Todd - A: English, B: New Zealander, C: Australian, or D: South African?

1007. Who won the Lance Todd Trophy in 1999, Mark Aston or Leroy Rivett?

1008. In what year did Sean Long win the Lance Todd Trophy for the second time?

1009. Who won the Lance Todd Trophy in 2005?

1010. In what year did Brian Lockwood win the Lance Todd Trophy - A: 1978, B: 1979, C: 1980, or D: 1981?

RUGBY LEAGUE WORLD CUP 2000

1011. The Rugby League World Cup 2000 was the first to feature a qualifying tournament. Which nations reached the qualifying play-off as a result?

1012. Which nation won the Rugby League World Cup 2000 qualifying play-off?

1013. Which nation did Fiji defeat 38-12 in its opening match of the Rugby League World Cup 2000?

1014. Which Australian player scored four tries as his side cruised to a 110-4 victory over Russia?

1015. Which nation did New Zealand defeat 84-10?

1016. Which two nations played out a 22-22 draw at the Millenium Stadium, Cardiff?

1017. Which future England Rugby Union international scored a hat-trick of tries as his side went on to beat Wales 58-18?

1018. Which nation won all of its Rugby League World Cup 2000 Group 3 games?

1019. Which nation won Group 4 of the Rugby League World Cup 2000?

1020. New Zealand Maori achieved its first ever Rugby League World Cup victory in 2000 against which nation in Group 4?

BEN COHEN

1021. In what year was Ben Cohen born?

1022. In what county was Ben Cohen born?

1023. England's footballing World Cup winner, George Cohen, is related to Ben in what way?

1024. Which French Rubgy Union club did Ben Cohen join in 2007?

1025. In what year did Ben Cohen make his debut for England?

1026. Ben Cohen's father, Peter, was killed in an incident at the nightclub he owned. What was the name of that establishment - A: Elite, B: Eternity, C: Enlightenment, or D: Enchantment?

1027. True or false: Ben Cohen is Jewish?

1028. Name one of the three nicknames by which Ben Cohen is best known.

1029. How many points did Ben Cohen score in his England career - A: 130, B: 140, C: 150, or D: 160?

1030. What was Ben Cohen's usual position on the rugby field?

RUGBY UNION WORLD CUP 2003

1031. Which player scored the most points in the Rugby Union World Cup 2003?

1032. Which nation did Australia beat 142-0?

1033. Which nation did England beat 84-6 in its opening match?

1034. When England beat South Africa 25-6 in their Pool C encounter, who scored the only try of the match?

1035. Who scored five tries in England's 111-13 victory over Uruguay?

1036. Which nation knocked South Africa out of the quarter-finals?

1037. Whom did England knock out of the quarter-finals?

1038. Which nation won the third place play-off?

1039. Who scored England's try in the final?

1040. Which two players are missing from this list of the starting line-up for England in the final - Josh Lewsey, Jason Robinson, Will Greenwood, Mike Tindall, Ben Cohen, Jonny Wilkinson, Matt Dawson, Lawrence Dallaglio, Richard Hill, Martin Johnson (c), Phil Vickery, Steve Thompson and Trevor Woodman?

WASPS

1041. In what decade was London Wasps founded?

1042. What is the name of Wasps' home ground?

1043. Where in Buckinghamshire is Wasps located?

1044. What is the predominant colour of Wasps' home shirts?

1045. How many times had Wasps been English champion when it won in 2004-05?

1046. How many times had Wasps won the Heineken Cup when it won it in 2006-07?

1047. Who did Ian McGeechan replace as Director of Rugby for Wasps in 2005?

1048. Who was the Wasps captain at the beginning of 2008?

1049. What was the name of the original rugby club that was split to form Wasps and Harlequins?

1050. At which London soccer ground did Wasps play home games for a while?

RONAN O'GARA

1051. In which nation was Ronan O'Gara born?

1052. What is Ronan O'Gara's nickname?

1053. Ronan O'Gara is best known for playing in what position?

1054. For which club side did Ronan O'Gara play?

1055. In what year did Ronan O'Gara make his international debut?

1056. On 11 February 2007, O'Gara scored the first Irish international try at which ground in the Six Nations loss to France?

1057. Ronan O'Gara scored all of Ireland's points in a 17-12 win over which side at Lansdowne Road on 13 November 2004?

1058. Ronan O'Gara's last-minute conversion against whom on 18 January 2003 helped his side to a 27-point victory, which took them through to the Heineken Cup quarter-final (the match became etched into Munster Rugby's folklore as the Miracle Match)?

1059. How many British and Irish Lions caps did Ronan O'Gara earn during two tours - A: 0, B: 1, C: 2, or D: 3?

1060. Who did Ronan O'Gara overtake to become Ireland's all-time top points scorer in 2006?

SALE SHARKS

1061. In what town is Sale Sharks based?

1062. In what decade was Sale Sharks founded?

1063. What is the name of Sale Sharks' home ground?

1064. What is the predominant colour of Sale Sharks' home shirts?

1065. Which Frenchman became the coach of Sale Sharks in 2004?

1066. In 2002 Sale Sharks went on to win the Parker Pen Shield at Oxford's Kassam Stadium, defeating which Welsh side 25-22?

1067. Sale Sharks took 20,000 fans to Twickenham for the 1997 Pilkington Cup final, but who won the match 9-3?

1068. Why did many Sale Sharks fans boycott the kit launched in 2006-07?

1069. When Sale Sharks won the European Challenge Cup against Pau 27-3, where was the match played?

1070. By what name is Sale Sharks' junior team known?

CLIFF MORGAN

1071. In what decade was Cliff Morgan born?

1072. Cliff Morgan is best known for playing in what position?

1073. For which club did Cliff Morgan play?

1074. In what year did Cliff Morgan last play for Wales - A: 1955, B: 1956, C: 1957, or D: 1958?

1075. Who was Cliff Morgan's opposing captain when he was on the BBC's *A Question of Sport?*

1076. How many British Lions caps did Cliff Morgan earn - A: 1, B: 2, C: 3, or D: 4?

1077. True or false: Cliff Morgan once produced the BBC's *Grandstand?*

1078. In what year was Cliff Morgan the subject of the TV series *This is Your Life* - A: 1968, B: 1978, C: 1988, or D: 1998?

1079. In what year was Cliff Morgan inducted into the Rugby Hall of Fame?

1080. What was the title of Cliff Morgan's 1996 autobiography written with Geoffrey Nicholson?

THE QUINNELLS

1081. Which Quinnell was born on 25 November 1983 in Llanelli, Wales?

1082. Which Quinnell was born on 20 August 1972 in Swansea?

1083. In what decade was Derek Quinnell born?

1084. What was the first English club that Craig Quinnell played for?

1085. Which Quinnell played for Worcester Warriors in 2007?

1086. How many caps did Derek Quinnell earn with Wales - A: 13, B: 23, C: 33, or D: 43?

1087. Which Quinnell once played Rugby League with Wigan Warriors?

1088. Who is the Quinnell that played 52 times for Wales?

1089. Which Quinnell's actual first name is Jonathon?

1090. Derek Quinnell is best known for playing in what positions?

MARTIN JOHNSON

1091. In what year was Martin Johnson born?

1092. What is Martin Johnson's middle name - A: Osborne, B: Buckingham, C: Kensington, or D: Hampton?

1093. Martin Johnson is best known for playing in what position?

1094. What is Martin Johnson's nickname?

1095. Martin Johnson played for which club?

1096. How many England caps did Martin Johnson earn - A: 54, B: 64, C: 74, or D: 84?

1097. How many British and Irish Lions caps did Martin Johnson earn between 1993 and 2001 - A: 4, B: 6, C: 8, or D: 10?

1098. In what year did Martin Johnson make his England debut?

1099. Martin Johnson's younger brother was also a top class rugby player. What is his name?

1100. Martin Johnson was preceded and succeeded by the same player as England captain. Who was that?

LONDON IRISH

1101. London Irish is known by what other name?

1102. In what decade was London Irish founded?

1103. What is the name of London Irish's home ground?

1104. What is the name of the Irish Wolfhound mascot of London Irish?

1105. London Irish won its first major trophy in 2002 when it won the Powergen Cup against which side?

1106. What is the name of London Irish's old home ground and its spiritual home?

1107. With which two clubs did London Irish merge in 1999?

1108. London Irish's largest home crowd was 22,648 when they played which team in the Guinness Premiership?

1109. True or false: there were no Irish players in the London Irish squad in 2007?

1110. What is the name of London Irish coach as at the beginning of 2008?

BARRY JOHN

1111. In what decade was Barry John born?

1112. Barry John was known by rugby fans by what nickname?

1113. Barry John is best known for playing in what position?

1114. Barry John broke what bone on a Lions tour to South Africa - A: fibia, B: humerus, C: collar bone, or D: jaw?

1115. In 1971 Barry John's Lions coach was from his hometown of Cefneithin. What was his name?

1116. Barry John scored 30 out of 48 points for the British Lions on tour against which nation?

1117. How many caps did Barry John earn with Wales - A: 25, B:35, C: 45, or D: 55?

1118. For what club did Barry John play?

1119. For what club did Barry John's brothers, Clive and Alan, play?

1120. Why did Barry John retire from rugby at the age of just 27?

JASON ROBINSON

1121. Jason Robinson was born in what city?

1122. What are Jason Robinson's three nicknames?

1123. In what year was Jason Robinson born?

1124. Jason Robinson is best known for playing in what position?

1125. For what club did Jason Robinson play before he joined Wigan Warriors?

1126. For what Rugby Union club did Jason Robinson make 16 appearances in 1996?

1127. In what year did Jason Robinson switch from Rugby League to Union?

1128. What award was bestowed on Jason Robinson in the 2008 New Year's Honours?

1129. What is the title of Jason Robinson's 2004 autobiography?

1130. On how many England caps did Jason Robinson end his career?

WILLIE JOHN McBRIDE

1131. In what decade was Willie John McBride born?

1132. What is Willie John McBride's real middle name?

1133. Willie John McBride was born in what county?

1134. Willie John McBride was awarded what by the Queen?

1135. Which Scot was Willie John McBride's partner at lock for the 1974 Lions tour of South Africa?

1136. In what year did Willie John McBride play his first Test against England at Twickenham?

1137. In what year did Willie John McBride score his first try for Ireland against France at Lansdowne Road?

1138. Following on from the previous question, what was the significance of that game for Willie John McBride?

1139. Willie John McBride was manager of the Lions tour in what year?

1140. In what year was Willie John McBride named as *Rugby World* magazine's Heineken Rugby Personality of the Century?

BATH

1141. In what decade was Bath RFC founded?

1142. What is the name of Bath's home ground?

1143. Which legendary Bath coach arrived at the club in 1978?

1144. With which club did Bath nearly merge in the early 2000s?

1145. In what year was the Official Supporters Club of Bath Rugby formed - A: 1977, B: 1987, C: 1997, or D: 2007?

1146. What river runs near to Bath's home ground?

1147. In what season did Bath first win the Courage League?

1148. How many times did Bath win the John Player/Pilkington Cup in the 1980s?

1149. Which club did Bath defeat in the 1998 Heineken Cup final?

1150. Which Australian joined Bath as coach in 2006?

GEORGE GREGAN

1151. In what nation was George Gregan born?

1152. In what year was George Gregan born?

1153. George Gregan is best known for playing in what position?

1154. For which French rugby club did George Gregan play?

1155. In what year did George Gregan make his international debut?

1156. In what year did George Gregan become captain of his country?

1157. Who did George Gregan replace as captain of Australia?

1158. For which Australian club did George Gregan play?

1159. George Gregan played his 100th Test against which nation?

1160. Who was Wallabies' coach when George Gregan won his 120th cap against England in Melbourne in 2006?

NEWCASTLE FALCONS

1161. In what decade was Newcastle Falcons formed?

1162. What is the name of Newcastle Falcons' home ground?

1163. What is the predominant colour of Newcastle Falcons' home shirts?

1164. Who took over control of Newcastle in the mid-1990s?

1165. In what year was Rob Andrew made Director of Rugby at Newcastle Falcons?

1166. What was the original name of Newcastle Falcons?

1167. In what year did Newcastle first win the National Cup?

1168. In the mid-1990s there was an attempt to merge NewcastleFalcons with local clubs from which three sports?

1169. True or false: Newcastle was the second fully professional Rugby Union club in the world in 1995?

1170. Who became chairman of Newcastle Falcons in 1999?

GLOUCESTER

1171. In what decade was Gloucester RFC founded?

1172. What is the name of Gloucester's home ground?

1173. What is the name of the hotel where Gloucester was
       formed - A: Spread Eagle Hotel, B: Red Eagle Hotel, C:
       Bald Eagle Hotel, or D: Golden Eagle Hotel?

1174. What is the predominant colour of Gloucester's home
       shirts?

1175. Which Italian became captain of Gloucester in 2006?

1176. In what season did Gloucester score the highest
       season's points tally in the Premiership (as of 2008)?

1177. Who became the owner of Gloucester in 1997?

1178. Which club did Dean Ryan coach before Gloucester?

1179. What were the traditional colours of Gloucester's home
       shirts before they adopted the current design?

1180. By what nickname is Gloucester often referred?

RUGBY UNION WORLD CUP 2007

1181. Although hosted by France, which other two nations staged matched in the 2007 Rugby Union World Cup?

1182. Which player scored the most points in the 2007 Rugby Union World Cup?

1183. Which team reached the quarter-finals of the 2007 Rugby Union World Cup along with Australia from Pool B?

1184. Which nation did New Zealand crush 108-13 in Pool C of the 2007 Rugby Union World Cup?

1185. Which nation did Scotland beat 42-0 in Pool C of the 2007 Rugby Union World Cup?

1186. Which player scored the most tries in the 2007 Rugby Union World Cup?

1187. Which nation will host the 2011 Rugby Union World Cup?

1188. Which nation did England defeat 12-10 in the 2007 Rugby Union World Cup quarter-final?

1189. Which nation did South Africa defeat 37-13 in the 2007 Rugby Union World Cup semi-final?

1190. What was the final score of the 2007 Rugby Union World Cup final?

THE LAST TEN

1191. Which Welsh international fly half won 87 caps and scored 1,049 points for his nation?

1192. Who did Phil Kearns replace as captain of Australia in 1995?

1193. Which Rugby Union club plays its home games at The Memorial Stadium?

1194. Which Rugby League club plays its home games at Hilton Park?

1195. Who was announced as manager of the Lions tour of South Africa in 2009?

1196. Which Great Britain Rugby League scrum half was born on 24 September 1976 in Wigan?

1197. Which French legend was born in Caracas, Venezuela, on 31 August 1958?

1198. Which Welsh rugby club plays its home games at St Helens Rugby and Cricket Ground?

1199. What is the colour of the home shirts of Cardiff RFC?

1200. Which Harlequins player played on 70 occasions for the All Blacks between 1995 and 2004?

ANSWERS

ORIGINS

1. 1845.
2. 1871.
3. 1895.
4. Blackheath Rugby Club (formed in 1858).
5. Edwin Ash.
6. 1871.
7. 20.
8. 1971.
9. 1922.
10. 1892.

WILLIAM WEBB-ELLIS

11. 1806.
12. 1823.
13. Brasenose College, Oxford.
14. Clergyman.
15. Ross McWhirter.
16. Matthew Bloxam.
17. Thomas Hughes.
18. Lancashire (Manchester).
19. 1872 (24 January).
20. Battle of Albuera.

RUGBY UNION WORLD CUP 1987

21. Australia and New Zealand.
22. 16.
23. Italy.
24. USA (beat Japan 21-18).
25. Grant Fox (126 points).
26. Mike Harrison.
27. Mark Ring.
28. Fiji.
29. France.
30. Gavin Hastings.

BRITISH AND IRISH LIONS

31. 1888.
32. Andy Irvine.
33. Finlay Calder.
34. John Dawes.
35. Willie John McBride.
36. Brian O'Driscoll.
37. 1993.
38. 1997 (versus South Africa).
39. Ian McGeechan.
40. Stephen Jones (Wales).

HISTORY OF RUGBY LEAGUE

41. The George Hotel.
42. Schism.
43. 1897.

44. *The two flankers.*
45. *Batley.*
46. *1929.*
47. *Manningham.*
48. *David Attenborough.*
49. *1971.*
50. *1981.*

GARETH EDWARDS
51. *Pontardawe.*
52. *1967.*
53. *1973.*
54. *Scrum half.*
55. *Cardiff.*
56. *Cliff Morgan.*
57. *20.*
58. *St David's shopping centre, Cardiff.*
59. *Owen.*
60. *Emlyn Hughes.*

ENGLAND
61. *1905.*
62. *1988 (Five Nations match versus Ireland at Twickenham).*
63. *Ireland.*
64. *Jonny Wilkinson.*
65. *Romania.*
66. *Australia.*
67. *Jason Leonard.*
68. *Rory Underwood.*
69. *Phil Vickery.*
70. *Jack Rowell.*

THE CHALLENGE CUP
71. *Murrayfield.*
72. *Bradford.*
73. *Lance Todd Trophy.*
74. *Hull Kingston Rovers.*
75. *Elland Road, Leeds United FC.*
76. *England, Scotland, Wales, France and Russia.*
77. *Sean Long (St Helens).*
78. *3 (1942-43, 1943-44 and 1944-45).*
79. *Featherstone Rovers.*
80. *8 (1987-88 until 1994-95).*

THE BARBARIANS
81. *Penarth.*
82. *Tony O'Reilly.*
83. *1890 (versus Hartlepool Rovers).*
84. *Scotland (74-31 victory in 2001 and 19-66 in 2006).*
85. *William Percy Carpmael.*
86. *Barbarians 27, New Zealand 13.*
87. *Leicester Tigers.*

88.	The Esplanade Hotel, Penarth.
89.	'Rugby Football is a game for gentlemen in all classes, but for no bad sportsman in any class.'
90.	England, Scotland, Wales, Ireland, New Zealand, Australia and South Africa.

TWICKENHAM

91.	Richmond upon Thames.
92.	The Cabbage Patch.
93.	1909.
94.	82,000.
95.	1937.
96.	2000 (Australia versus England, Rugby League World Cup).
97.	St Helens (beat Bradford Bulls 13-6).
98.	St Helens (beat Huddersfield Giants 42-12).
99.	1996.
100.	Erica Roe.

HULL KINGSTON ROVERS

101.	New Craven Park.
102.	1989.
103.	1922-23.
104.	1977-78.
105.	1979-80.
106.	1983-84.
107.	Bath Rugby.
108.	Mark O'Neill.
109.	A crown.
110.	The Robins.

WORLD CUP 1991 (UNION)

111.	Ralph Keys (Ireland).
112.	Japan.
113.	New Zealand.
114.	USA.
115.	Canada.
116.	Western Samoa.
117.	Mark Ring.
118.	Ireland.
119.	Rob Andrew.
120.	Tony Daly.

JONNY WILKINSON

121.	Italy (February 2008).
122.	Surrey.
123.	Fly half and inside centre.
124.	Newcastle Falcons.
125.	Rob Andrew.
126.	The Times.
127.	Northumbria University.
128.	2003.
129.	His right (although he was predominantly left footed).

130.   Adidas.

EDDIE WARING
131.   1910.
132.   It's a Knockout.
133.   'It's an up and under.'
134.   Dewsbury.
135.   The Morecambe and Wise Christmas Show 1977.
136.   Mike Yarwood.
137.   'He's a poor lad!'
138.   'He's goin' for an early bath!'
139.   1981.
140.   1986.

WOMEN'S RUGBY
141.   1891.
142.   106.
143.   1930.
144.   1986.
145.   1994.
146.   1991.
147.   Wales.
148.   USA.
149.   England.
150.   New Zealand.

THE ALL BLACKS
151.   Grey.
152.   Sean Fitzpatrick.
153.   Japan (June 1995).
154.   Australia (August 1999).
155.   Doug Howlett.
156.   The Haka.
157.   Andrew Mehrtens (967 points).
158.   1884.
159.   Joe Rokocoko.
160.   Richie McCaw.

CATALAN DRAGONS
161.   Perpignan Dragons Rugby League Football Club - Catalan Dragons.
162.   2001.
163.   Stade Gilbert Brutus.
164.   France.
165.   Michael Potter.
166.   Wigan Warriors.
167.   2004 and 2005.
168.   XIII Catalan Club and Saint Estève.
169.   Clint Greenshields.
170.   3 years.

CARDIFF ARMS PARK
171.   1958.

172. Frank Bruno.
173. False. It was the name of both grounds. The park they were situated on was Cardiff Arms Park.
174. The River Taff.
175. Glanmore's Gap.
176. Glamorgan County Cricket Club.
177. Cardiff Athletic Club.
178. The Cardiff Arms Hotel, which was demolished in 1878.
179. Great Park.
180. 53,000.

RORY UNDERWOOD
181. Tony Underwood.
182. Leicester Tigers.
183. RAF pilot.
184. 1963.
185. Middlesbrough.
186. 85.
187. Bedford.
188. Wing.
189. 49.
190. Rob Andrew.

ANDREW JOHNS
191. New South Wales.
192. Halfback.
193. Warrington Wolves.
194. Anterior cruciate ligament injury.
195. 21.
196. Newcastle Knights.
197. Canberra Raiders.
198. Kicking coach.
199. Possession of Ecstasy.
200. 2001.

GAVIN HASTINGS
201. Andrew Gavin Hastings.
202. Edinburgh.
203. Big Gav.
204. Scott.
205. Fullback.
206. OBE.
207. France.
208. Cambridge.
209. C: 733.
210. 1990.

THE SPRINGBOKS
211. White.
212. Percy Montgomery.
213. Uruguay.
214. England.

215. *1995 and 2007.*
216. *John Smit.*
217. *Jake White.*
218. *South Africa 36, England 0.*
219. *Australia and New Zealand.*
220. *Argentina.*

MURRAYFIELD STADIUM
221. *Edinburgh.*
222. *1925.*
223. *Murrayfield Ice Rink.*
224. *Haymarket.*
225. *67,800.*
226. *Connor Milligan.*
227. *£50 million.*
228. *Toulouse and Stade Français (Toulouse won 18-12).*
229. *Heart of Midlothian.*
230. *Wales.*

SIR CLIVE WOODWARD
231. *Cambridgeshire (Cambridge).*
232. *Harlequins.*
233. *Leicester Tigers.*
234. *Soccer.*
235. *Centre.*
236. *C: 2.*
237. *1997.*
238. *Southampton.*
239. *Winning!*
240. *Bachelor of Arts degree in Sports Science (followed by a Postgraduate Certificate in Education [PGCE]).*

MARTIN OFFIAH
241. *1966.*
242. *London.*
243. *Widnes.*
244. *Chariots.*
245. *Wigan.*
246. *2003.*
247. *5.*
248. *1997.*
249. *London Broncos.*
250. *A Blaze of Glory.*

HARLEQUINS
251. *London Broncos.*
252. *Twickenham Stoop.*
253. *The Hampstead Football Club.*
254. *Wasps.*
255. *1988.*
256. *The European Shield.*
257. *2005.*

258. 2006.
259. The Lexus Stand.
260. Dean Richards.

WALES
261. Warren Gatland.
262. 1881.
263. Japan.
264. Rowland Williams.
265. Neath.
266. Scotland.
267. Swansea (St Helens Ground).
268. England.
269. 1987.
270. Neil Jenkins.

ENGLISH RUGBY UNION LEAGUE CHAMPIONSHIP
271. 1987.
272. Courage.
273. Leicester Tigers.
274. Sale Sharks.
275. Allied Dunbar.
276. Bath and Leicester Tigers.
277. London Wasps.
278. Gloucester.
279. 1994-95.
280. Leeds Tykes.

THE GRAND SLAM
281. Win all of its Six Nations matches during one year's competition.
282. B: 1 (1948).
283. Wales.
284. 1960s (1968).
285. 1980s (1984).
286. 3 (1971, 1976 and 1978).
287. 1997 and 1998.
288. 3 (1925, 1984 and 1990).
289. England (1991, 1992 and 1995).
290. England (26-19), Scotland (30-15), Italy (47-8), Ireland (16-12) and France (29-12).

JONATHAN DAVIES
291. Carmarthenshire.
292. 1962.
293. Neath and Llanelli.
294. C: 32.
295. Widnes.
296. 1996.
297. North Queensland Cowboys and Canterbury Bulldogs.
298. Cardiff.
299. 1997.
300. Fly half.

RUGBY LEAGUE WORLD CUP 1954-1960
301. France.
302. Great Britain, France, New Zealand and Australia.
303. France and Great Britain.
304. Australia.
305. France.
306. Australia.
307. Great Britain.
308. Bradford (Odsal Stadium).
309. Great Britain.
310. Australia.

RAY GRAVELL
311. Raymond William Robert Gravell.
312. Mynydd-y-garreg.
313. Grav.
314. Llanelli.
315. 1975.
316. 1985.
317. Up n Under.
318. Damage.
319. 4.
320. Málaga, Spain.

MILLENNIUM STADIUM
321. 74,500.
322. 1999.
323. Dad.
324. Liverpool (beat Arsenal 2-1).
325. Doncaster Rovers (beat Bristol Rovers 3-2 after extra time).
326. 2001, Speedway Grand Prix of Great Britain.
327. True.
328. Arsenal and Southampton.
329. South Africa (26 June 1999).
330. 2002 (Leicester Tigers beat Munster 15-9).

DAVID CAMPESE
331. Ian.
332. 1962.
333. Fullback and wing.
334. D: hairdresser.
335. Queanbeyan.
336. Campo.
337. New Zealand.
338. Wales.
339. 1987 World Cup.
340. Alan Jones.

LAWRENCE DALLAGLIO
341. 1972 (10 August).
342. Bruno.
343. Wasps.

344. South Africa.
345. No. 8 or Flanker.
346. MBE.
347. The sinking of the pleasure boat *Marchioness* on the River Thames.
348. 2004 (August).
349. Italy and Ireland (his father was Italian and his mother was Irish).
350. 1993.

BILL McLAREN
351. 1923.
352. Hawick near the English border.
353. Royal Artillery.
354. Tuberculosis.
355. Physical education.
356. 1953.
357. D: Wales (Wales won 12-0).
358. 1959.
359. Aberdeen.
360. 2002.

RUGBY SCHOOL
361. 1560s (1567).
362. B: Laurence Sheriff.
363. Warwickshire.
364. Queen Elizabeth I.
365. Anglican.
366. C: 11-18.
367. A: teacher.
368. B: Lawrence Llewelyn-Bowen.
369. B: 1975.
370. D: School House.

ST HELENS
371. A red oval with an S wrapped around an H.
372. Knowsley Road.
373. C: 1873.
374. Hull Kingston Rovers.
375. White Shirts with red trim.
376. Daniel Anderson.
377. Ellery Hanley.
378. Liverpool.
379. Blue.
380. Kel Coslett.

RUGBY LEAGUE POSITIONS
381. Prop forward (left).
382. 5 (right wing) and 2 (left wing).
383. 10.
384. Right centre.
385. 1.
386. Second row.
387. Loose lock/forward.

388. 9.
389. Scrum half/halfback.
390. 6.

J.P.R. WILLIAMS
391. Bridgend.
392. 1940s (1949).
393. Orthopaedic surgeon.
394. John Peter Rhys.
395. 1969.
396. Tennis (he beat future professional David Lloyd in the final held at
the   All England Lawn Tennis and Croquet Club).
397. False. They were not related.
398. Bridgend or London Welsh.
399. C: 55.
400. Fullback.

RUGBY LEAGUE WORLD CUP 1968-1970
401. Australia and New Zealand.
402. New Zealand.
403. Sydney Cricket Ground.
404. France (20-2).
405. Brisbane.
406. Great Britain.
407. Great Britain.
408. Leeds.
409. Australia.
410. New Zealand.

CALCUTTA CUP
411. 1879.
412. 20.
413. Dean Richards (England) and John Jeffrey (Scotland).
414. Jonny Wilkinson (England).
415. No one, as it was a draw on both occasions.
416. Inverleith.
417. 1930s (1930).
418. 18-12.
419. False. Scotland won 13-7 in 1990.
420. True.

ELLERY HANLEY
421. 1961.
422. The Black Pearl or Mr Magic.
423. Leeds.
424. Loose forward.
425. Bradford Northern.
426. Leeds.
427. 1990.
428. £150,000.
429. 13.
430. Balmain Tigers.

TRIPLE CROWN
431. Ireland (2007).
432. The Invisible Cup.
433. England (23 as of 2007).
434. Scotland.
435. Ireland.
436. Wales (1976-1979).
437. False. England won in 1980.
438. True: 1965, 1969, 1971, 1976-1979.
439. Scotland (1938).
440. C: 1913.

WARRINGTON
441. Cheshire.
442. The Wire, Wolly Backs or The Wolves.
443. Primrose and blue.
444. 1870s (1879).
445. Halliwell Jones Stadium.
446. Wilderspool.
447. 1947-48.
448. Lord Doug Hoyle of Warrington.
449. York Wasps.
450. 1973-74.

PARC DES PRINCES
451. Princes' Park.
452. Paris Saint-Germain (PSG).
453. B: 1897.
454. A: velodrome (cycling track).
455. B: the city of Paris.
456. 1924.
457. 2 (League in 1954 and Union in 2007).
458. 1998.
459. Stade Français.
460. D: 48,712.

FRIK DU-PREEZ
461. South Africa.
462. 1961 (versus England).
463. Lock/flanker.
464. 1930s (28 November 1935).
465. Northern Transvaal.
466. Australia (1971).
467. British Lions (1968).
468. Danie Craven.
469. Rustenburg, South Africa.
470. England (on his debut in 1961).

ANDY FARRELL
471. Wigan.
472. 2004.
473. 1975.

474. *1993.*
475. *2004.*
476. *Wigan.*
477. *Saracens.*
478. *Newcastle Falcons.*
479. *Inside centre.*
480. *Fly half.*

JASON LEONARD
481. *1968.*
482. *Barking in Essex.*
483. *Prop.*
484. *Saracens.*
485. *118 (a record).*
486. *George Gregan (Australia).*
487. *1990 (versus Argentina).*
488. *The Fun Bus.*
489. *Carpenter.*
490. *Harlequins.*

BRADFORD BULLS
491. *Bradford Northern.*
492. *1881.*
493. *Grattan Stadium (Odsal Stadium).*
494. *1934.*
495. *1948-49.*
496. *1977-78.*
497. *Peter Hood.*
498. *The Great Betrayal.*
499. *1963.*
500. *Paul Deacon.*

JONAH LOMU
501. *1975.*
502. *Cardiff Blues.*
503. *Wing.*
504. *1994.*
505. *Gold.*
506. *Kidney.*
507. *New Zealand Order of Merit.*
508. *2002.*
509. *All-time top try scorer with 15 tries.*
510. *France.*

GAVIN HENSON
511. *Bridgend.*
512. *Centre, fly half or fullback.*
513. *Lloyd.*
514. *Ospreys.*
515. *My Grand Slam Year.*
516. *Ruby Megan.*
517. *Train.*

518.   Swansea.
519.   2001.
520.   Japan (2001).

BILL BEAUMONT
521.   1950s (9 March 1952).
522.   Lock.
523.   1975.
524.   Roger Uttley.
525.   D: Blackledge.
526.   Chorley.
527.   1978.
528.   1980.
529.   Wooden Spoon.
530.   1996.

CHRIS PATERSON
531.   Edinburgh.
532.   Fullback, wing or fly half.
533.   Mossy.
534.   Gloucestershire Rugby.
535.   Andy Irvine.
536.   1999.
537.   Earn his 50th cap.
538.   Edinburgh.
539.   Gavin Hastings.
540.   Dan Parks.

GILBERT
541.   1820s (1823).
542.   James Gilbert.
543.   A: 1877.
544.   In the High Street next to Rugby School.
545.   Grays of Cambridge.
546.   Pig's bladder.
547.   C: 1978.
548.   1995.
549.   James Gilbert.
550.   True.

RUGBY LEAGUE WORLD CUP 1972
551.   France.
552.   New Zealand.
553.   France.
554.   New Zealand.
555.   It was a draw (10-10).
556.   Lyon.
557.   False. They didn't play any games in Paris.
558.   Australia.
559.   A: Stade De Gerland.
560.   C: 4,500.

NIGEL STARMER-SMITH
561.   *1940s (25 December 1944).*
562.   *Scrum half.*
563.   *Harlequins.*
564.   *Teacher.*
565.   *B: 7.*
566.   *Rugby World.*
567.   *Rugby Special.*
568.   *1969 (versus South Africa).*
569.   *Hockey.*
570.   *True.*

BRYAN HABANA
571.   *Mister Kardinaal, Jet Shoes, Habernero or Dash.*
572.   *Bryan Robson (former Manchester United footballer).*
573.   *1983 (12 June).*
574.   *Wing.*
575.   *2004.*
576.   *8 (a record shared with Jonah Lomu).*
577.   *Bulls.*
578.   *Gary Bailey (Manchester United's former goalkeeper who grew up
in   South Africa).*
579.   *2007.*
580.   *Cheetah.*

CASTLEFORD TIGERS
581.   *Yorkshire (West Yorkshire to be precise).*
582.   *The Jungle.*
583.   *1920s (1926).*
584.   *Wheldon Road.*
585.   *1992-93.*
586.   *Argos.*
587.   *Jack Fulton.*
588.   *Rochdale.*
589.   *St Helens.*
590.   *Danny Orr.*

RUGBY UNION POSITIONS
591.   *Loosehead prop.*
592.   *2.*
593.   *Inside centre.*
594.   *3.*
595.   *Number 8.*
596.   *4 and 5.*
597.   *Openside flanker.*
598.   *Right wing.*
599.   *10.*
600.   *Fullback.*

PHIL VICKERY
601.   *1976.*
602.   *D: milkman.*

603. Martin Corry.
604. Devon (Barnstaple).
605. Prop.
606. Gloucester.
607. Wasps.
608. Raging Bull.
609. 1998 (versus Wales).
610. A: John.

FRANCE RUGBY UNION TEAM
611. Les bleus, Les tricolores or XV de France.
612. A rooster on a red shield.
613. Fabien Pelous.
614. Serge Blanco.
615. Marc Lièvremont.
616. Lionel Nallet.
617. Christophe Lamaison (380).
618. C: New Zealand.
619. C: Brazil.
620. Quarter-finals.

HULL FC
621. A: 1865.
622. Airlie Birds or Black and Whites.
623. KC Stadium.
624. The Gene Autry song, 'Old Faithful'.
625. BBC2 Floodlit Trophy.
626. 1919-20.
627. Clive Sullivan.
628. Sheffield Eagles.
629. Bradford Bulls.
630. 1982-83.

SUPER LEAGUE
631. 1996.
632. Rupert Murdoch.
633. Paris Saint Germain.
634. Cheshire.
635. Australia.
636. National League 1.
637. Castleford Tigers.
638. Hull Kingston Rovers.
639. 2002.
640. 2005.

NATIONAL LEAGUE CLUB HOME GROUNDS
641. Oldham Roughyeds.
642. Salford Reds.
643. Sheffield Eagles.
644. Widnes Vikings.
645. Leigh Centurions.
646. Batley Bulldogs.

647. *Featherstone Rovers.*
648. *Celtic Crusaders.*
649. *Halifax RLFC.*
650. *Dewsbury Rams.*

THE NATIONAL LEAGUE
651. *Celtic Crusaders.*
652. *Lose by 12 points or less.*
653. *The Co-operative Group.*
654. *The Northern Ford Premiership.*
655. *2003.*
656. *Chorley Lynx.*
657. *2003 and 2006.*
658. *London Skolars.*
659. *Rochdale Hornets and Doncaster Lakers.*
660. *Salford City Reds.*

SIX NATIONS CHAMPIONSHIPS
661. *1880s (1883).*
662. *1893.*
663. *1910.*
664. *1931.*
665. *Scotland (30-15), Italy (47-8) and France (29-12).*
666. *Giuseppe Garibaldi Trophy.*
667. *1993.*
668. *2000.*
669. *Scotland.*
670. *An outbreak of foot and mouth disease in England.*

WRU CHALLENGE CUP
671. *1972.*
672. *Neath (beat Llanelli 15-9).*
673. *Llandovery.*
674. *Llanelli (1973-1976).*
675. *Pontypool.*
676. *Llanelli (13 times as of 2007).*
677. *Caerphilly.*
678. *They scored more tries.*
679. *Llanelli.*
680. *Newport.*

LLANELLI RFC
681. *Blue.*
682. *1870s (1872).*
683. *Stradey Park.*
684. *Scarlets.*
685. *New Zealand.*
686. *Little Saucepan.*
687. *A rag doll.*
688. *Derek and Scott Quinell.*
689. *Four (1991, 1992, 1993 and 1998).*
690. *1992-93.*

RUGBY LEAGUE WORLD CUP 1975

691. England and Wales. Great Britain was split up to take advantage o
      a glut of Welsh talent at the time.
692. St Helens Rugby and Cricket Ground, Swansea.
693. Wales (14-7).
694. New Zealand.
695. Headingly, Leeds.
696. France.
697. England (16-13 in Wigan).
698. Carlaw Park, Auckland.
699. Sydney Cricket Ground.
700. Australia (beat England).

HUDDERSFIELD GIANTS

701. 1860s (1864).
702. 1895 (the year that Huddersfield became founder member of the
      Northern Rugby Football Union).
703. Fartown.
704. Galpharm Stadium, shared with Huddersfield Town FC.
705. Claret and gold.
706. Jon Sharp.
707. 1950s (1952-53).
708. Blackpool Gladiators.
709. 1960s (1961-62).
710. Sheffield Eagles.

ANDY IRVINE

711. 1950s (1951).
712. 1972 (versus New Zealand).
713. Fullback.
714. C: Robertson.
715. Scottish Rugby Union (SRU).
716. B: 1976.
717. A: chartered surveyor.
718. Heriot's Former Pupils.
719. MBE.
720. 1982 (versus Australia).

LESLEY VAINIKOLO

721. 1979 (4 May).
722. Tonga.
723. The Volcano.
724. New Zealand.
725. Bradford Bulls.
726. Wing.
727. Gloucester Rugby.
728. Wales.
729. Canberra Raiders.
730. Hull.

WAKEFIELD TRINITY WILDCATS

731. 1870s (1873).

732. *1999.*
733. *Belle Vue.*
734. *Huddersfield Giants.*
735. *Shane McNally.*
736. *Castleford Tigers.*
737. *Thornes Park.*
738. *1966-67 and 1967-68.*
739. *1962-63.*
740. *Jamie Rooney.*

WILL CARLING
741. *B: 1965 (12 December).*
742. *1988 (16 January).*
743. *Soldier with the Royal Artillery.*
744. *Harlequins.*
745. *Centre.*
746. *Diana Princess of Wales.*
747. *22 years.*
748. *Bum Face (relating to his cleft chin).*
749. *Julia Carling.*
750. *C: 72.*

IRELAND
751. *The Shamrock.*
752. *Croke Park.*
753. *New Zealand.*
754. *False. Malcolm O'Kelly is.*
755. *The Oval.*
756. *Quarter-finals (four times).*
757. *Ronan O'Gara (over 800 points).*
758. *USA (Ireland won 83-3).*
759. *Eddie O'Sullivan.*
760. *Brian Ashton.*

RUGBY LEAGUE WORLD CUP 1977 AND 1985-88
761. *Carew Park, Auckland.*
762. *France.*
763. *John Kolc.*
764. *Australia 13, Great Britain 12.*
765. *Christchurch.*
766. *Papua New Guinea.*
767. *New Zealand.*
768. *France.*
769. *Great Britain.*
770. *New Zealand.*

DAN CARTER
771. *Canterbury.*
772. *1980s (1982).*
773. *DC.*
774. *Fly half.*
775. *2003.*

776. 2005.
777. Canada.
778. Christchurch.
779. South Africa.
780. Wales.

WIGAN WARRIORS
781. Red and white hoops.
782. D: castle.
783. 1870s (1872).
784. JJB Stadium.
785. Brian Noble.
786. Dave Whelan.
787. 1998.
788. St Helens.
789. Andy Goodway.
790. Stuart Fielden.

RUGBY UNION WORLD CUP 1995
791. South Africa.
792. Ivory Coast (Côte d'Ivoire).
793. England and France (France won 10-9).
794. Ellis Park (approximately 62,000 capacity).
795. South Africa.
796. Argentina.
797. Ireland.
798. Thierry Lacroix.
799. Wales.
800. New Zealand.

JOE LYDON
801. 1960s (1963).
802. 1975.
803. Widnes.
804. 1983.
805. B: £100,000.
806. 1984.
807. D: 262.
808. Technical director.
809. Waterloo.
810. Backs coach.

SARACENS
811. A: 1876.
812. Watford.
813. Sarries or The Men in Black.
814. Vicarage Road.
815. Nigel Wray.
816. Neil de Kock.
817. Richard Hill.
818. Marylebone.
819. Japan.

820.   Chris Jack.

WIDNES VIKINGS
821.   Stobart Stadium Halton.
822.   Warrington Wolves.
823.   1870s (1873).
824.   The Chemics.
825.   Steve O'Connor.
826.   Farnworth & Appleton Cricket and Football Club.
827.   A: 7.
828.   Castleford Tigers.
829.   Steve McCormack.
830.   1977-78.

JEREMY GUSCOTT
831.   D: 1965.
832.   Bath.
833.   Bricklayer.
834.   British Gas.
835.   Centre.
836.   1989.
837.   Tonga.
838.   Romania.
839.   B: 65.
840.   The BBC.

ITALY
841.   1920s (1929).
842.   Spain.
843.   Czech Republic.
844.   South Africa.
845.   Stadio Flaminio.
846.   Azzurri or The Gladiators of Rome.
847.   Nick Mallett.
848.   Sergio Parisse.
849.   Alessandro Troncon (101 caps).
850.   Scotland and Wales.

GREAT BRITAIN RUGBY LEAGUE
851.   White.
852.   The Lions.
853.   New Zealand (1908).
854.   Fiji.
855.   2002.
856.   David Waite.
857.   The Ashes.
858.   Brian Noble.
859.   Tony Smith.
860.   Maurie Fa'asavalu.

PAUL GRAYSON
861.   1971 (30 May).

862. Lancashire (Chorley).
863. Fly half.
864. Northampton Saints.
865. 1995.
866. A: Western Samoa.
867. Larry or Grase.
868. C: 32.
869. 2004.
870. 400.

LEEDS RHINOS
871. 1860s (1864).
872. Carnegie.
873. Brian McClennan.
874. Ronnie the Rhino.
875. Twice (2005 and 2008).
876. 2004.
877. Eleven.
878. Blue.
879. Bradford Bulls.
880. D: Harold Buck.

JON WEBB
881. D: 1963.
882. B: London.
883. Webby.
884. A: Bristol.
885. Fullback.
886. Bristol and Bath.
887. 1987.
888. 2 (1987 and 1991).
889. A: 296.
890. Orthopaedic surgeon (Webb now runs the Jonathan Webb Clinic).

RUGBY LEAGUE WORLD CUP 1989-1992
891. D: Mount Smart Stadium, Auckland (23 July 1989; New Zealand 14, Australia 22).
892. New Zealand.
893. Papua New Guinea.
894. Australia.
895. New Zealand.
896. Central Park, Wigan.
897. The Boulevard, Kingston-upon-Hull.
898. C: 14.
899. True.
900. Wembley Stadium.

ROB ANDREW
901. Yorkshire (Richmond).
902. Squeaky.
903. Fly half.
904. Cricket.

905. Two (1991 and 1995).
906. Wasps.
907. Jonny Wilkinson.
908. Newcastle Gosforth.
909. C: 71.
910. Director of Elite Rugby.

LEICESTER TIGERS
911. 1880s (1880).
912. Welford Road.
913. Seven (1988, 1995, 1999, 2000, 2001, 2002 and 2007).
914. 2001.
915. Marcelo Loffreda.
916. Gloucester.
917. False. It was originally planned but never happened.
918. Green.
919. Martin Corry.
920. Chalkie.

BRIAN O'DRISCOLL
921. 1979.
922. D: Gerald.
923. BOD, Drico, The Dricmeister General and God.
924. Leinster.
925. 1999.
926. 2001.
927. Outside centre.
928. 2005.
929. France.
930. Scotland.

2008 SIX NATIONS
931. Sergio Parisse.
932. Jonny Wilkinson.
933. Vincent Clerc.
934. Chris Paterson.
935. Andrea Marcato.
936. Tommy Bowe.
937. Vincent Clerc.
938. Danny Cipriani.
939. Ronan O'Gara.
940. Martyn and Shane.

CHARLIE HODGSON
941. 1980 (12 November).
942. Halifax.
943. Sale Sharks.
944. Fly half.
945. A: Christopher.
946. 2001.
947. Cruciate.
948. C: 44.

949.   Centre.
950.   University of Durham.

RUGBY LEAGUE WORLD CUP 1995
951.   United Kingdom.
952.   Ten.
953.   England.
954.   England, Australia, Fiji, South Africa, New Zealand, Tonga, Papua New Guinea, Wales, Western Samoa and France.
955.   Fiji (versus South Africa).
956.   Tonga and Papua New Guinea (drew 28-28).
957.   England, Wales, Australia and New Zealand.
958.   Andrew Johns.
959.   Old Trafford, Manchester (England versus Wales).
960.   Australia.

STACEY JONES
961.   1976.
962.   Scrum half.
963.   NZ Warriors.
964.   Catalan Dragons.
965.   The Little General.
966.   1995.
967.   Maunga Emery.
968.   2007.
969.   NZ Warriors.
970.   2002.

DUSTY HARE
971.   1950s (29 November 1952).
972.   William.
973.   England.
974.   Fullback.
975.   Nottinghamshire.
976.   1974.
977.   Wales.
978.   South Africa.
979.   Leicester.
980.   Farmer.

RUGBY UNION WORLD CUP 1999
981.   Wales.
982.   Gonzalo Quesada.
983.   Argentinian.
984.   Spain.
985.   New Zealand.
986.   Tonga.
987.   Namibia.
988.   Fiji.
989.   Japan.
990.   South Africa.

WILL GREENWOOD
991.   1972 (30 October).
992.   Lancashire (Blackburn).
993.   Dick (Richard).
994.   Centre.
995.   Harlequins (1994-96 and 2000-06).
996.   Leicester Tigers.
997.   1997.
998.   Ireland.
999.   2006.
1000.   A: 3

LANCE TODD TROPHY
1001.   Man of the Match in the Challenge Cup final.
1002.   Jason Robinson.
1003.   Paul Wellens and Leon Pryce.
1004.   D: Billy Stott.
1005.   Martin Offiah (1992 and 1994).
1006.   B: New Zealander.
1007.   Leroy Rivett.
1008.   2004 (versus Wigan).
1009.   Kevin Sinfield.
1010.   C: 1980.

RUGBY LEAGUE WORLD CUP 2000
1011.   USA and Lebanon.
1012.   Lebanon.
1013.   Russia.
1014.   Wendell Sailor.
1015.   Cook Islands.
1016.   Lebanon and Cook Islands.
1017.   Lesley Vainikolo.
1018.   Papua New Guinea.
1019.   Ireland.
1020.   Scotland.

BEN COHEN
1021.   1978 (14 September).
1022.   Northamptonshire.
1023.   Uncle.
1024.   CA Brive.
1025.   2000.
1026.   Eternity.
1027.   False (though his ancestors may have been).
1028.   Big Ben, Air Ben or Benji.
1029.   C: 150.
1030.   Wing.

RUGBY UNION WORLD CUP 2003
1031.   Jonny Wilkinson.
1032.   Namibia.
1033.   Georgia.

1034. Will Greenwood.
1035. Josh Lewsey.
1036. New Zealand (29-9).
1037. Wales (28-17).
1038. New Zealand (beat France 40-13).
1039. Jason Robinson.
1040. Ben Kay and Neil Back.

WASPS
1041. 1860s (1867).
1042. Adams Park.
1043. High Wycombe.
1044. Black.
1045. Five (1989-90, 1996-97, 2002-03, 2003-04 and 2004-05).
1046. Twice (2003-04 and 2006-07).
1047. Warren Gatland.
1048. Lawrence Dallaglio.
1049. Hampstead Football Club.
1050. Loftus Road (Queens Park Rangers FC).

RONAN O'GARA
1051. USA (San Diego, California).
1052. ROG.
1053. Fly half.
1054. Cork Constitution or Munster (either will do).
1055. 2000.
1056. Croke Park.
1057. South Africa (Springboks).
1058. Gloucester.
1059. B: 1.
1060. David Humphreys.

SALE SHARKS
1061. Stockport.
1062. 1860s (1861).
1063. Edgeley Park.
1064. Blue.
1065. Philippe Saint-André.
1066. Pontypridd.
1067. Leicester Tigers.
1068. Because it did not display the crest with the year the club was founded.
1069. Kassam Stadium in Oxford.
1070. Jets.

CLIFF MORGAN
1071. 1930s (1930).
1072. Fly half.
1073. Cardiff.
1074. A: 1955.
1075. Henry Cooper.
1076. D: 4.

1077. True.
1078. C: 1988.
1079. 1997 (one of the inaugural inductees).
1080. *Cliff Morgan: Beyond the Fields of Play.*

THE QUINNELLS
1081. Gavin Quinnell.
1082. Scott Quinnell.
1083. 1940s (22 May 1949).
1084. Saracens.
1085. Gavin Quinnell.
1086. B: 23.
1087. Scott Quinnell.
1088. Scott Quinnell.
1089. Craig Quinnell.
1090. Lock forward or No. 8.

MARTIN JOHNSON
1091. 1970.
1092. A: Osborne.
1093. Lock.
1094. Jonno.
1095. Leicester Tigers.
1096. D: 84.
1097. C: 8.
1098. 1993.
1099. Will Johnson.
1100. Lawrence Dallaglio.

LONDON IRISH
1101. The Exiles.
1102. 1890s (1898).
1103. Madejski Stadium.
1104. Digger.
1105. Northampton.
1106. The Avenue in Sunbury.
1107. London Scottish and Richmond.
1108. London Wasps.
1109. Eoghan Hickey, Bob Casey, Aidan McCullen and Jeremy Staunton.
1110. Brian Smith.

BARRY JOHN
1111. 1940s (6 January 1945).
1112. The King.
1113. Fly half.
1114. C: collar bone.
1115. Carwyn James.
1116. New Zealand.
1117. A: 25.
1118. Cardiff.
1119. Llanelli.
1120. He didn't want to be in the public eye anymore.

JASON ROBINSON

1121. Leeds.
1122. Billy Whizz, Robbo and Stumpy.
1123. 1974 (30 July).
1124. Wing.
1125. Hunslet.
1126. Bath.
1127. 2000 (he joined Sale Sharks).
1128. OBE.
1129. *Finding My Feet.*
1130. 51.

WILLIE JOHN McBRIDE

1131. 1940s (6 June 1940).
1132. James.
1133. County Antrim.
1134. MBE.
1135. Gordon Brown.
1136. 1962.
1137. 1975.
1138. It was his last game for Ireland.
1139. 1983.
1140. 2004.

BATH

1141. 1860s (1865).
1142. The Rec (Recreation Ground).
1143. Jack Rowell.
1144. Bristol.
1145. C: 1997.
1146. Avon.
1147. 1988-89.
1148. Five (1984, 1985, 1986, 1987 and 1989).
1149. Brive.
1150. Steve Meehan.

GEORGE GREGAN

1151. Zambia.
1152. 1973 (19 April).
1153. Scrum half.
1154. Toulon.
1155. 1994.
1156. 2001.
1157. John Eales.
1158. Brumbies.
1159. South Africa.
1160. John Connolly.

NEWCASTLE FALCONS

1161. 1870s (1877).
1162. Kingston Park.

1163. Black.
1164. Sir John Hall.
1165. 1995.
1166. Gosforth.
1167. 1976.
1168. Soccer (Newcastle United FC), basketball (Eagles) and ice hockey (Wasps [later Riverkings, Jokers, Vipers, etc.]).
1169. False. They were the first.
1170. Dave Thompson.

GLOUCESTER
1171. 1870s (1873).
1172. Kingsholm Stadium.
1173. A: Spread Eagle Hotel.
1174. Red.
1175. Marco Bortolami.
1176. 2002-03 (82 points).
1177. Tom Walkinshaw.
1178. Bristol.
1179. Red and white hoops.
1180. Cherry and Whites.

RUGBY UNION WORLD CUP 2007
1181. Wales and Scotland.
1182. Percy Montgomery (South Africa).
1183. Fiji.
1184. Portugal.
1185. Romania.
1186. Bryan Habana.
1187. New Zealand.
1188. Australia.
1189. Argentina.
1190. South Africa 15, England 6.

THE LAST TEN
1191. Neil Jenkins.
1192. Michael Lynagh.
1193. Bristol.
1194. Leigh Centurions.
1195. Gerald Davies.
1196. Sean Long.
1197. Serge Blanco.
1198. Swansea.
1199. Sky blue.
1200. Andrew Mehrtens.

www.apexpublishing.co.uk